Praise for The Alchemy of Combat

"With wisdom, compassion and devotion, Larry Decker has been treating combat veterans of all wars from WWII to Afghanistan for three decades. In *The Alchemy of Combat*, he shares the gems for healing that he has distilled from this important work. Larry passes far beyond symptom reduction and civilian readjustment to map the path by which veterans can achieve a new identity and worldview, affirm the value of trauma, embrace full consciousness of their military history, and achieve a new level of spirituality that adheres to their highest ideals. *The Alchemy of Combat* is an important discourse on the value of trauma and its underlying spirituality, as well as an excellent "how-to" guidebook on practicing therapy with former combatants."

Edward Tick, Ph.D.
Author of *War and the Soul* and *Warrior's Return*
Executive Director, Soldier's Heart, Inc.

"*The Alchemy of Combat* is a must read for veterans, anyone working with veterans, or those who want to understand the combat experience and the emotional/spiritual injuries that can result. Ultimately, spiritual transformation heals all wounds, and Dr. Larry Decker clearly has dedicated his professional life to supporting this process in veterans, beautifully capturing the process in this book."

Dr. Keith Witt,
Author of *Integral Mindfulness* and *Waking Up*

"I have been working with combat veterans and their loved ones since 1995. Although plenty of books have been published about helping families 'adjust' to life after combat, this is the best book I have ever read that truly addresses the deepest levels of spiritual healing that warriors need. Importantly, *The Alchemy of Combat* provides clinicians with a skillful guide for how to walk with combat veterans and caregivers on this journey towards Posttraumatic Growth. Dr. Decker includes numerous case examples, which provide rare glimpses into the psyche of combat veterans from WWII to Afghanistan, along with his insightful interventions in response to their deep sharing. He then offers exercises that provide ways for clinicians and clients to develop their own abilities to grow and heal at different stages. The book is firmly grounded in theories that are incredibly rich and complex yet are presented in a manner that is straightforward and clear. Clinicians who are newer, as well as those experienced in holding the therapeutic space for wounded warriors, will learn how to increase their capacity to more effectively work with combat veterans from Dr. Decker's wise and compassionate guidance."

Kirsten Olson, Ph.D.
Clinical Psychologist
Santa Barbara, California

"As brave as the soldiers who risk their lives during battle, so are those therapists who accompany them as they attempt to heal from the traumas of war that rage on in their psyches long after combat has ended. For more than thirty years psychologist Larry Decker, Ph.D., has assisted veterans suffering from the ravages of PTSD depression, rage, shame, and substance abuse readjust to civilian life. But as he reveals in this compelling book, for those veterans who have braved death, the loss of friends, and extreme physical suffering, ordinary life is simply not enough. Through the deeply moving stories of veterans he has worked with over the years, Decker shows how ancient spiritual wisdom adds a vital missing dimension to conventional therapeutic techniques. Through this powerful alchemy, veterans are able to achieve 'post-traumatic growth' by discovering what they most desperately yearn for: a renewed sense of purpose to equal what they felt in military service, and the gold of meaning concealed within the depths of their suffering. *The Alchemy of Combat* is must reading for every citizen who cares about the fate of America's vets."

Pythia Peay
Psychology and spirituality journalist
Author of *American Icarus: A Memoir of Father*
and *Country and America on the Couch:
Psychological Perspectives on American Politics and Culture*

"*The Alchemy of Combat*" is a brilliant work showing how true healing for the combat veteran integrates compassion for others and oneself through spirituality and by helping to create the ideal self. I have known Dr. Decker for seventeen years while working for the Veterans Affairs Administration with combat veterans, and, at times, sharing clients. His treatment approach works. He has taken a very complex subject of Posttraumatic Stress Disorder and made it intuitively easy to understand, whether you are the veteran, a family member, friend or a therapist who wants to gain more insight into the inner world of the combat veteran. He provides exercises that are easy to use and powerful. The veterans often say they think they have lost their soul. Dr. Decker's work helps guide them to their Posttraumatic Growth. He clearly explains how to use his method for growth and shows you how to help the veteran not only reintegrate back into the world, but shows ways to find purpose and the ability to again serve society.

Sharon L. Rapp, Ph.D
Clinical Psychologist
Santa Barbara, California

The ALCHEMY of COMBAT

The ALCHEMY *of* COMBAT
Transforming Trauma in Combat Veterans

A Guide for Therapists,
As Well as Family, Friends, Loved Ones,
Colleagues, and Others Who Care

Larry R. Decker

Sulūk Press
New Lebanon New York

Published by
Sulūk Press, an imprint of
Omega Publications, Inc.
New Lebanon NY
www.omegapub.com

Cover design by Sandra Lillydahl
Cover image courtesy of Shutterstock.com
Statue of David by Michelangelo Buonarroti

This edition is printed on acid-free paper that meets ANSI
standard X39–48.

Larry R. Decker (1941–)
The Alchemy of Combat:
Transforming Trauma in Combat Veterans
A Guide for Therapists, as Well as Family, Friends, Loved Ones,
Colleagues, and Others Who Care

Includes foreword, introduction, appendix, glossary
1.Decker, Larry R. 1941–.
2. Combat—Psychological Aspects 3. Soldiers—Psychology
4. Veterans—Psychology 5. Veterans—Mental Health
II. Title

Library of Congress Control Number: 2014949189

Printed and bound in the United States of America
ISBN 978–1-941810064

DEDICATION

You know who you are.
Warriors, therapists, relatives, friends, seekers—
may you find your purpose and meaning.

Contents

Contents

Contents

Contents

List of Meditation Practices

FOREWORD

Around fifteen years ago I was in a school cafe-
teria in Santa Barbara, California, waiting my
turn to see one of the psychologists who were putting
on a free public workshop for people with job stress.
My wife had asked me to go because for the past ten
years I'd become increasingly irritable, raging at the
children, doing odd things like pounding a hammer
through a wall in a rage, taking out a series of kitchen
cabinets with my fists in a rage. One time, I climbed
on the hood of a car in an intersection, trying to kick
in its windshield because the driver had startled me
by honking when I was slow off the mark. When I got
my turn a young psychologist listened to my litany of
symptoms of "stress" including the ones above. Then
he looked at me and asked, "Were you ever in a war?"
Suddenly there was only me, him, and memories of
my tour in Vietnam as a Marine. I started sobbing. I
don't mean crying; I mean anguished snot-coming-
out-of-my nose sobbing. When I finally got it together he said, "You have posttraumatic stress disorder.
Ever heard of it?" I had not. Pulling out his business
card and writing the name Larry Decker, on its back,

along with an address on Santa Barbara Street, he said, "You need to see this man immediately—not tomorrow, not next week—now. I am going to call him so he'll be expecting you."

I stumbled my way to the Veterans Outreach Center where Larry worked, and there I met this extraordinary healer of psyches and souls.

Larry asked me to tell my story. The first time I got through my entire military history in two sessions. The second time took months. Then there was a third time with a group. One day, after seeing Larry for over a year, he said, "I've never seen anyone fully come to terms with their PTSD without some kind of spiritual component. It's time for you to do this. I don't care if it's transcendental meditation, Buddhism, or the Mormon Church."

What he said is true because combat not only wounds your body and mind; it wounds your soul. I found that spiritual path and with varying degrees of diligence follow it to this day—and I have come to terms with my time at war and its resulting post-traumatic stress.

Our nation from time to time asks its young people to kill, after years of having been told "Thou shalt not kill." Taking human life should be the role of the gods. We ask nineteen-year-olds to do it. Not once in all my training for combat was this aspect of killing even mentioned. My wife and children lived with turmoil, heartbreak, and, sometimes, fear for nearly thirty years before I ended up in that veterans outreach center. Had I known what Decker taught me there, that suffering would have been greatly reduced.

Larry Decker's experience with thousands of veterans and his years of spiritual discipline and training are distilled in this book. If you are a therapist, a family member, or an individual dealing with war trauma, I will give you the equivalent advice given to me so long ago, "You need to read this book immediately— not tomorrow, not next week—now."

Karl Marlantes
Lieutenant, United States Marine Corps
Navy Cross
Author of *Matterhorn*
and *What It Is Like To Go To War*

ACKNOWLEDGEMENTS

Thank you to my wife Beverly for your ongoing insight and support. Thank you to Naomi Rose, book developer, for developing a manuscript into a book. Thank you to Karl Marlantes for your early review (which was invaluable) and your ongoing friendship. Thank you to the early editors: Betsy Quinn, Shams Kairys, and Fran Davis. Thank you to all of the endorsers and your kind words. Thank you to Pir Zia for your help and support. Thank you to the Omega Publications staff for believing in the work and your wonderful creativity.

COMBAT

Southeast of Da Nang, Vietnam, surrounded by mountains, a squad of Marines were parked in their Armored Personnel Carrier (APC) along a swiftly flowing river. On the other side of the river was a valley of desiccated rice paddies. It was 1967, and the heat waves vibrated up across the valley.

In the far distance the Marine sergeant saw what appeared to be a herd of water buffalo moving rapidly across the valley. He pulled out the binoculars and looked more carefully. Now he saw that the herd was actually a large group of North Vietnamese Army (NVA) soldiers. The soldiers were running across the open space but were burdened down with mortars, rockets, and heavy equipment. The Sergeant shouted, "Fuck man, it's the NVA!!"

APCs have several different types of weapons including .05 Howitzers, .50 caliber and .30 caliber machine guns, grenade launchers, and, of course, the troops had M16 rifles. Marines are very good shots. The group of NVA was about one hundred yards away.

The sergeant, after accounting for several dead, watched through his binoculars as the remnants of the NVA force tried to get to the high ground to set up mortars, only to be killed by the machine guns.

There were no survivors.

ALCHEMY

Good Friday

At one time
Good Friday meant the coming of the weekend
as did all those Fridays during Lent,
those premature hot afternoons
during the Stations of the Cross
when I held my breath in laughter
after Jimmy Mallard farted,
so as not to get drug out of the pew
by Sister Amadeus pinching my ear,
and the incense waved about the sanctuary
by Father O'Connor became the scent of
Spring, heralding the coming of Summer,
the release from this tomb of the sixth grade.

At one time
Good Friday became a dried rice paddy
where the air rose in vibration
with heat and moisture and fear,
and those sixty men
across the river, moving over the field
so weighted down with mortars,
and rockets and weapons
we first thought were water buffalo,
now caught, with no cover,
in our sights as we fired round after round
and watched them struggle
through their last moments.

Alchemy

At one time
Good Friday will become a day of atonement,
regardless of that mystical Jew crucified
for all our sins,
where in the premature summer heat
I will sit somewhere on a patio
telling stories to my grandchildren
and when they ask me about the war
I will not draw details in black and white,
or paint the colors mutilation,
I will not try to describe the smell of death,
but I will speak in my kindest voice
about how cruel we can be to one another,
about how very sad war is.

Sergeant Bruce Schmidt,
United States Marine Corps
March 18, 2012

INTRODUCTION

There are those who go to war and those who don't. Those of us who don't are told by those who do that combat is a chaotic, bloody, horrible mess that many men, and some women, nevertheless, believe is an ultimate experience. However, after the adrenalin of battle has waned, the shaking has subsided, and the veteran has returned "home," many combat veterans experience the downsides of that "ultimate experience": depression, anger, and the overwhelming feelings of grief and anxiety. That emotional aftermath of war we now characterize as a psychological disorder: Posttraumatic Stress Disorder (PTSD).

That is to say, many soldiers see war as the ultimate experience within a military context; but once they are out of the military and back in civilian life, their emotional wounds make it difficult for them to re-enter "normal" life, nor do we civilians have a way to integrate them as part of the culture. At the same time, it's likely that they actually did have an "ultimate," even transcendent experience. Veterans tell us that war was the most meaningful time of their lives, a time when they mattered, when what they did had purpose and meaning.

In exploring the cultural and psychological disruptions within veterans that manifests as PTSD, *The Alchemy of Combat* suggests that the therapists who work with veterans' symptoms and suffering can help them go beyond simply adapting back into society. If we, as therapists, are going to honor veterans' experiences, it is important not to simply try to help them adjust to civilian life but to also help them use what they learned in combat to be more conscious, effective, and powerful individuals in civilian society. Out of their combat PTSD can come Posttraumatic Growth (PTG)—in other words, an increase in awareness, greater compassion, and a deeper understanding of life.

While this book is primarily addressed to therapists who treat veterans or may do so in the future, it's my hope that what's here will also be of interest and practical use to others in veterans' lives—their families, friends, loved ones, colleagues, support groups, and so on. Therefore, if you are among the latter, I hope you will focus on those areas in this book that illuminate your understanding, increase your compassion, and offer some ways to be of genuine help to veterans in their growth, even if you are not a therapist.

Posttraumatic Stress Disorder (PTSD)

There is considerable knowledge about PTSD in the psychological technical literature, and in the historical accounts of war's impact on the human psyche. We have evidence that veterans from all wars, dating back to ancient India, experience those emotions that we list as symptoms of the disorder. These symptoms include intrusive thoughts, depression, panic attacks, fear of loss of control, survivor guilt, nightmares, avoidance of memories, and anger.

Certainly those postwar emotions are difficult, but perhaps they are to be expected and, viewed in the context of war, not necessarily pathological. But we don't observe veterans in war—we experience them in civilian life. In our civilian world, an exaggerated startle response to a loud noise is clearly just what was said: "exaggerated." Yet to veterans, their response (diving to the ground) is completely normal and probably saved their lives in the context of war. By calling veterans' emotional aftermaths "PTSD," we emphasize that civilian society is "normal" and veterans' culture is to be isolated, contained within the military.

We pathologize emotions that, given the veteran's experiences, are predictable and normal; we therefore expect those emotions to be debilitating and interfering in veterans' lives.

The Possibility of Growth and Transformation

It seems almost heretical to propose that there could be emotional growth from such experiences as killing, even if in the name of a government.

But there are clues galore, such as in the veterans' descriptions of combat as the time when they were most alive. Maybe it is true, as Chris Hedges asserts in *War is a Force That Gives Us Meaning*, that war takes us out of our ordinary lives and opens up our feelings to an awareness beyond the mundane.[1]

---

1 Hedges, Christopher. *War Is A Force That Gives Us Meaning*, (New York: Public Affairs, 2002).

I have been working with combat veterans for over thirty years in both Veterans Administration and private practice settings. Joe was one of the thousands of veterans I have treated for PTSD. When he first walked in the door of my office, I noticed his tattoos, large Egyptian scarabs, covering the undersides of his arms. He was a tough guy, a former Marine who had served two tours in Iraq.

Joe's previous treatment for his PTSD, by another trauma therapist, had been well-intentioned and had reduced the intensity of Joe's torments. Of course that treatment had been focused on helping Joe adjust to civilian society. But Joe's agony was not to be undone by simply adjusting to society and its ordinary life.

"I went to see this guy who was the expert in PTSD. He was OK, but I don't think he got me. I'm not going to live like everybody else. Not after what I've seen and done. He wanted me to go to school, and you know all the rest of that. I've tried sitting in class. Can't do it. Too many sounds and pictures in my head. Man it's a real movie in here. What do you think? Can you do anything?" Joe looked at me intently.

He was open for help, searching to connect with someone. His life had been changed by Iraq, and he wasn't going back to how he had been before his combat, but he was still in chaos, unable to make sense of his new reality.

"Yeah, there's more to life than just making money, having a family, and even more to it than an interesting career that makes you want to get up in the morning," I responded.

"Hey I would settle for that if I could. That doesn't sound so bad." Joe expressed his paradox, his wanting the peace of consciously working towards a purpose and yet being unable to adjust to how society seemed to demand his conformity.

The effect of combat on the human psyche is paradoxical. Combat destroys understanding, produces overwhelming grief, demolishes beliefs into chaos, creates decades of fixated emotional development—and at the same time, mixed in with a deeper understanding of life, a desire for something profound, and an almost desperate need for meaning. Veterans with their experiences of war are no longer satisfied with just melting back into the American culture. They demand authenticity and are quick to spot duplicity. Combat veterans understand the thirteenth century Sufi poet, Rumi, when he says, "Be as you appear; appear as you are."[2]

Veterans are in chaos but they are also in clarity. If we only see their chaos then we miss their insights. In order to treat their chaos, therapists have to recognize their understanding. The anger of veterans emerges partly from their inability to communicate their insights, awareness, teamwork, camaraderie, and self-sacrifice. If they are given the opportunity to value their actions, then their anger may be transformed into fruitful outrage, moving from personal umbrages into inspiration for salvaging the downtrodden.

What's Missing from Current Treatment Approaches

Contemporary treatment for PTSD is effective. Cognitive exposure (the current, most effective treatment), if done with care and sensitivity, will reduce the severity of symptoms, calm the chaos, and enable

2 Jalal ad-Din Rumi (1207–1273).

veterans to be relatively successful in the civilian world. If veterans want a "regular life," then cognitive exposure psychotherapy can help that happen.

Not that exposure treatment is easy. Exposure treatment is a method to help veterans confront their traumatic memories. Exposure treatment requires veterans to relive their combat experience and have a willingness to feel what they didn't have time to feel during the war. Exposure treatment can be challenging and painful. But if veterans are sufficiently willing, that treatment can reduce anger, decrease depression, and reduce the frequency of panic attacks.

But there is more than just helping veterans adjust to civilian life. If treatment has as its focus emotional and behavioral adjustment, then the value of the trauma is negated. If veterans are simply retrained to be proper civilians and to reduce their inner anguish, then their combat is reduced to a pathological experience instead of a transformative one.

There are two related forms of treatment that purport to essentially ameliorate the emotions of traumatic memories, if not completely erase the memory. Eye Movement Desensitization Reprocessing (EMDR) and Thought Field Therapy (TFT) have become the treatment of choice by many veterans. These treatments bypass the confrontation of memories and, instead, purport to reduce the emotionality of the memories without the reliving required in the exposure forms of treatment. Given the veterans' testimonials and several outcome studies, those treatments appear to be effective in reducing pain and anxiety. Certainly attempting to reduce the pain of the memory is laudable, but not if done by taking away conscious awareness.

I am reminded of the Gordian Knot. In this myth, if you could untie the knot you would become the ruler of Asia. As some legends have it, Alexander the Great simply took out his sword and sliced it open. Perhaps the knot was a symbol of our lives, and if we could unravel the mystery of our existence we would rule our inner world. The therapies EMDR and TFT seem more like Alexander's sword than the loosening of our knotted minds.

If there is not a repression of emotion, not a decrease of conscious memory, and not a denial of experience in treatment, then veterans' anger can be transformed into productive outrage, their depression can be a healing withdrawal into the inner life, and their anxiety can turn into excitement for life's possibilities.

Veterans tell us that war was the most meaningful time of their lives, a time when they mattered, when what they did had purpose and meaning. Iraq veterans tell me they want to go back to the war, not just for their comrades, but because what they did in Iraq meant something.

If we are going to honor veterans' experiences, as mentioned earlier, it is important not to simply try to help them adjust to civilian life, but to also help them use what they learned in combat to be more conscious, effective, and powerful individuals in civilian society. Out of their combat PTSD can come Posttraumatic Growth (PTG)—or, in other words, an increase in awareness, greater compassion, and a deeper understanding of life.

What I Have Learned from
My Experience of Treating Veterans

For over thirty years, I have treated combat PTSD in veterans of all wars from WWII to Afghanistan. I have trained numerous interns and other counselors in this method of treatment. I have presented technical papers at scholarly conferences and published technical articles in the journals of trauma treatment.

In my work I have found that simply helping veterans adjust to contemporary society does not take advantage of the alchemy of combat. Alchemy means that there is a transformation of the personality as a result of traumatic experiences. Combat changes worldviews. That change of view gathers and mixes the experiences of sudden death, mangled bodies, and unpredictable tragedy, with heroic self-sacrifice.

But veterans with PTSD are hesitant to acknowledge their uplifting of spirit in their willingness to sacrifice, their inspiration in overcoming horrible challenges, and their dedication to higher ideals. Because of veterans' despair over their killing, they retreat from those higher experiences, believing themselves to be unworthy of those feelings of honor. Instead they choose to adopt the relative security of a flat worldview dominated by society's values of technology and pleasure.

The suggestions for treating combat PTSD, explored in this book, not only help veterans adjust to civilian life; it also helps them use their experiences to find their meaning and their purpose. Inherent in meaning and purpose is the spiritual nature, the manifesting of the highest ideals.

Bringing a Spiritual Approach to Treatment of Combat Trauma

How can we combine contemporary methods of treatment of combat trauma with spiritual teachings? This is not a new question. The use of an ancient Buddhist meditation technique (mindfulness training) to change cognitions is already in use in many therapy settings.

However, simply changing cognitions does not satisfy the soul's search for awakening. Alchemy is not a bloodless transformation of the personality but a dynamic transcendence that awakens our inner depths.

In *The Handbook of Posttraumatic Growth*, edited by Lawrence Calhoun and Richard Tedeschi, there is a mention of the teachings of Buddha, Christ, Islam, and the Greek philosophers as evidence of "the possibilities for meaning and change emerging from the struggle with tragedy, suffering, and loss."[3] However, for the next 363 pages there is not another mention of the deep wisdom and knowledge found in those teachings.

A more integrative view of trauma is found in Karen Armstrong's *The Great Transformation*[4] where she describes the timelessness of the spiritual paths and how the teachings and lives of the main figures in those paths have shown us how to use the inherent

---

3 Calhoun, Lawrence & R. G, Tedeschi, *Handbook of Post-traumatic Growth: Research and Practice* (Charlotte: Lawrence Erlbaum Associates, 2006).

4 Armstrong, Karen, *The Great Transformation: The Beginning of Our Religious Traditions.* (New York: Alfred A. Knopf, 2006).

traumas of life to improve our existence and transcend the ordinary.

The Alchemy of Combat uses the power of spiritual teachings to form a basis for treatment of combat PTSD. The roots of treatment that honor and use combat experiences to discover meaning and purpose are found in all of the spiritual paths, but especially in ecstatic Sufi teachings. Those roots are discovered through the melting of inner rigidity. As Rumi writes:

> *Today, like every other day, we wake up empty*
> *and frightened. Don't open the door to the study*
> *and begin reading. Take down the dulcimer.*
> *Let the beauty we love be what we do.*
> *There are hundreds of ways to kneel and*
> *kiss the ground.[5]*

I am a student of Sufism, and my approach to treatment is completely intertwined with my spiritual practice. As Sufism is the spiritual path I know most intimately, it will largely be from the Sufi teachings that I draw to illustrate and suggest the healing that deep spirituality can bring; however, I invite you to draw from the wisdom of your own spiritual tradition, spurred by these Sufi teachings and examples, if you are so moved. Along with case histories, therapeutic dialogue, and descriptions of traumatic events in the lives of veterans, I will also include in this book my experiential study of alchemy, the "royal art of transformation." In service of this goal, I have included the use of prayer, meditation, and breath as essential ingredients in the furthering of PTG.

---

5 Moyne, John & Coleman Barks, *Open Secret: Versions of Rumi* (Putney: Threshold Books, 1984) 37.

The Alchemical Process

The alchemy of combat is a process of breakdown and renewal (i.e., *solve et coagule*: dissolve and reform) where beliefs and egos are shattered and soldiers' ideas about the world and themselves are thrown into chaos. From that breakdown can come either veterans' desperate attempts to adjust to civilian life or their discovery of a transcendent awareness that transforms them into leaders.

Through the alchemy of the interacting forces of ego dynamics and belief systems, the chaos of combat can create a transcendent awareness. In treatment, those dynamics are used to help veterans widen beliefs—not only to integrate their combat trauma, but also to use that trauma to create meaning and purpose. When veterans' beliefs expand to integrate their trauma, a more three-dimensional worldview becomes available that provides inspiration and uplifting happiness for the soul. As the Sufis say, "We do not live by bread alone, we need wine."

A Note about Names and Dialogues

The therapy dialogues portrayed in the book are based on my treatment with veterans. Fictitious names are used to protect confidentiality. For any stories that come from sources not my own, I provide a footnote. Any quotation not noted was received in personal communication.

But what happened to Joe, the dangerous-looking and unsettled veteran, mentioned at the beginning? Joe moved out of my area and went back to school, where he struggled with relationships with other students, teachers, and administration. I occasionally heard from Joe's therapists, hospital staff, and Joe himself, about his struggles. Then I received a phone call from a mutual friend that Joe had been shot and killed by his roommate.

He had survived countless dangers in the military only to meet a violent end to his physical life in his country. There is nothing guaranteed about this treatment process, just like everything in life.

And yet, there is reason for hope. Just as Joe struggled with his darkness only to be undone by the pervasive violence in our culture, there are also hundreds of thousands of men and women who have overcome, integrated, and transcended the traumatic memories of combat.

࿋

At the end of the talk someone from the audience asked the Dalai Lama, "Why didn't you fight back against the Chinese?" The Dalai Lama looked down, swung his feet just a bit, then looked back at us and said with a gentle smile, "Well war is obsolete, you know." Then after a few moments, his face grave, he said, "Of course the mind can rationalize fighting back...but the heart, the heart would never understand. Then you would be divided in yourself, the heart and the mind, and the war would be inside you."

PART I
MAKING CHOICES

He was unprepared for being neither dead nor at home.

Chapter One
The Mystic Wine

Solve et coagule: dissolve and reform
The alchemical secret

Since you are properly a clod, you will not rise into the air;
you will rise into the air if you break and become dust.
I was snow and I melted, so that the earth drank me,
till I became a mist of soul that I might climb to the sky.

Unknown Dervish

The Eastside of Santa Barbara, in 1972, was filled with families and neighborhood barbecues. Ed, home from Vietnam for over two months, was still in war. His mother had learned quickly not to touch him awake in the morning.

His first morning home, she had come into his bedroom and joyfully hugged him. When she found herself on the floor, Ed was on top of her, his hands around her throat, and she started to scream. He came to himself and moved off and away from her. He cried and apologized. She frantically left the room.

This morning Ed woke, still with the smell of the jungle and the noise of mortars. He gradually oriented to his room, remembered he was in his parents' house, and began thinking about the death of his best friend in Vietnam. The man died on a patrol when Ed was a short-timer with only a few days left on his tour of duty. On the day Sam died, Ed had refused any further patrols; and because Ed's tour would soon be ending, the sergeant went along with it. Then Sam was killed, on a patrol that Ed should have been on.

Ed got up, went to the refrigerator, and found a beer. He upended the can draining the contents. He found another and drank half of it before settling into his morning. His parents were at work and he was alone in the house.

By midmorning Ed had drunk two six-packs and was beginning to overcome his memories when there was a knock on the door. He pulled the window curtain aside and looked out at the front porch.

It was Joey and Louie, his cousins. They knew each other from childhood, but now things were different. To the cousins Ed seemed jumpy, even a little scary.

Ed let them in and they all hugged. Louie told him there had been a serious beating of another cousin by a group that lived on the Westside of Santa Barbara. They needed Ed's help.

"All of those assholes are at a barbecue right now. I mean they put Vince in the hospital, man! But they're over there thinking they are such tough shit." Louie was irate and obviously out for revenge.

Ed listened, then asked, "What do you want to do?" Louie pulled out a handgun. "We drive by their barbecue and waste their main man," he shrugged. But when Ed saw the pistol, his mind left Santa Barbara, his cousins, their problems, and the country.

He was sitting in the helicopter on his steel pot, waiting to descend to the landing zone (LZ). It was a hot LZ and there was a lot of shit flying about. He could see the basketball-sized globs of fire going past the chopper. The door gunner had the M60 machine gun on full throttle, and the pilot fired the rockets as they moved into the LZ. Suddenly there was a hole in front of him. A patch of light where before there was none. The man beside him fell over and blood spurted everywhere. Everybody was yelling and the noise of the guns was unbelievable.

The helicopter pilot had gotten the chopper a few feet from the ground of the LZ and the crew chief was yelling at the grunts to jump. Ed jumped into tall elephant grass, with a full pack, hundreds of rounds of ammunition, his M16, grenades, and canteens. He fell through the grass trying to protect his face from getting cut by the grass blades. Rounds were snapping past him and tracers were coming from the tree line. The grass was deep, and he fell about ten feet, landing awkwardly, twisting his ankle, and cursing the pilot.

"Ed! Hey ED!" Ed slowly realized that he was in the front room of his parents' home with his cousins. They were both looking at him like he was a strange alien life form. "Sure," he said. "Let's go get the fuckers."

The Westside is about ten minutes from the Eastside. Santa Barbara is not an enormous city. The three men attracted little attention as they entered the Westside barrio in their nondescript car.

They drove by the barbecue in the front yard of a well-kept home. "See, the guy with the red bandana around his head. That's the main asshole," Louie said from the back seat. The three men continued driving down the street. Ed said, "Give me the weapon."

Louie handed him the pistol. Ed made sure there was a round in the chamber and said, "Let's do it."

Joey was driving and he slowly made a U-turn. Now Ed was on the side next to the house. He pulled the handgun up to the open window, and put the red bandana in his sights. He pulled the trigger, but nothing happened. The gun misfired. Ed swore and said, "Get the fuck out of here."

When the Dragon's Fire of Combat Melts the Psyche

Ed's ideas about life are different than civilians' ideas. His cousins, the Westside group, and his parents all believe that life is predictable. When a person does something, several things might happen; but those things are all expected. This is not true for Ed. He doesn't know what to believe, what to expect. He only knows that he doesn't know. The dragon's fire of combat melted his psyche, changing his ways of seeing the world.

In combat, formerly obdurate belief systems become liquid and are no longer available in that previous predictable sense. After combat, what was once trusted and seen as real is no longer reliable. Only one's weapon and one's comrades are real; nothing else is dependable.

Ed misses his squad, his men, his knowing that it would end and he would be either dead or at home. He was unprepared for being neither dead nor at home. Now he knows that the dragon's fire never ends.

Several years after the incident with the gun misfiring, Ed came in for treatment with me to the Vet

Center where I worked. He had continued living a violent, alcoholic existence, landing in and out of jail.

Other therapists had focused on his substance abuse. In the early 1980s, Posttraumatic Stress Disorder (PTSD) was not a well-known diagnosis. Sitting across from me, Ed complained, "They kept saying that drinking was my problem. Like if I stopped drinking, all of that other shit would just go away."

I asked him, "Have you ever talked about Vietnam?"

He looked a bit surprised and said, "No. What's the point? Why open up that can of worms?"

I offered, "It seems like that's what you think about the most. Maybe if we talked about it, you might not have to think about it all the time."

Ed said, "You're the Doc. If you think that will help, sure let's try it. What I'm doing sure isn't working."

Ed's previous therapists had wanted him to adjust to civilian life. That was like asking him to change his citizenship to that of a foreign country. He knew things they didn't, but they believed they knew better. Ed didn't know how to tell them that they were full of shit, except to use those words. The other therapists of course interpreted Ed's responses as "resistance."

Taking me up on my invitation, Ed began to teach me about Vietnam. Being a civilian, I could not compare my experience to his. I am neither a REMF (rear echelon motherfucker) nor (later, when I worked with veterans of Iraq) a FOBBIT (someone who never left the Forward Operating Base). Even more importantly, I never experienced combat and I have no military training. I am a civilian. I represent the population that Ed encounters every day. And so Ed

29

got to be the expert on his own experiences, perhaps for the first time.

What I learned from Ed has only been reinforced, as well as expanded, over the years. Currently, my therapy practice is filled with veterans from the U.S. wars in Vietnam, Iraq, and Afghanistan. They flood my office. Veterans from the more recent wars in Iraq and Afghanistan, young men and women, are still vibrating with the smells and sounds of pain, blood, body parts, killing, and heroism. "What is the matter with me?" they ask with grief-filled eyes. They don't understand why they feel so alone and confused.

Posttraumatic Stress Disorder: The "Never World"

For veterans caught in the "never world" between combat and civilian life—never able to be a civilian and never able to be in combat—mental health professionals constructed a label, Posttraumatic Stress Disorder (PTSD). Less clinically, the military prefers to call it "combat fatigue," "shell shock," and, most recently, "battle-mind training."

Regardless of what the difficulties are called, it is clear that veterans have been changed. And although these changes may be disturbing and painful, within the context in which they arose they also seem quite reasonable.

If you have been trained by the military to work within a disciplined unit that has killing an enemy as its purpose, you have been changed. If you have been deployed to a combat zone and have experienced people trying to kill you, you have been changed. If you have tried to kill the enemy, if you have killed the enemy, and if you have witnessed people around you being killed and wounded, you have been changed.

The military's purpose is to change belief systems so that individuals may be able to kill other individuals. This phase takes place during training. The actual killing further changes beliefs. The traumatic nature of killing and seeing others killed creates chaos in soldiers' beliefs. Those chaotic belief systems persist into civilian life, and are labeled as PTSD.

The diagnostic label PTSD has both positive and negative aspects. On the positive side, it gives a name to a group of difficulties that are disrupting and interfering in veterans' lives. Having awareness of this label also helps give some comfort to veterans who feel overwhelmed by their symptoms. Many veterans have expressed great relief to hear that their anguish and grief has a name and is treatable.

On the negative side, the PTSD label pathologizes what is really a normal human response to killing and terror. As Arthur Egendorf mentioned in *Healing From the War*,[1] PTSD is the result of ordinary people experiencing extraordinary suffering.

PTSD symptoms manifest as intrusive thoughts, depression, panic attacks, fear of loss of control, survivor guilt, nightmares, avoidance of memories, and anger. Those experiences plague veterans and interfere with their ability to have an effective life.

However, as indicated in the Introduction, there may also be a transcendent aspect. Combat experiences

---

1 Egendorf, Arthur. *Healing From the War: Trauma and Transformation After Vietnam.* (Boston: Houghton Mifflin, 1985).

may also result in a growth of veterans' ability to inspire and lead in civilian life. Some combat veterans are able to be touched by the violence without being overwhelmed. Instead, the experience of combat stimulates latent qualities of awareness, enabling soldiers to actually improve emotional functioning.

Sometimes those qualities emerge in the political world, where individuals elected to high office have directly experienced the bloody reality of combat. While being elected to political office does not necessarily mean that the veteran avoided PTSD, it does mean that somehow the veteran was able to overcome the complete debilitating nature of the disorder.

I had the opportunity to meet one of those veterans-turned-politicians who had not only overcome his combat-related emotional difficulties, but he had also overcome the loss of one of his legs. This person, Jim, told me that his mother may have been responsible for his apparent ability to transcend his pain.

"When I got back, my mother came to see me in the hospital every day. Even during my physical therapy and my learning how to walk with the prosthesis, she would show up. Somehow she knew what I needed to do, and she insisted, each day, that I tell her, in detail, everything that had happened. I think that was what has enabled me to do what I do."

He was a very successful politician and businessman, and even made a run at the presidency. One of the last bits of insight he gave me was, "You know, we were young men. They only send young men, because older men would think too much. When you work with veterans, tell them to remember what they were like when they were young, and to love that person."

32

That man didn't adjust to society; he used the power of his experiences to make society adjust to him. What is it that makes him the exception? It is easy to list his intelligence, his very enlightened parents, his excellent education, and his privileged cultural background. However, there are others like Jim who came from similar backgrounds, who succumbed to the despair and bitterness that marks PTSD. The real question, then, is not why is Jim different, but how might we, as therapists, help our combat veterans find that same resilience that he was able to contact?

While Ed was overwhelmed by his rage and his grief, Jim used those same emotions to lead and inspire. His combat transformed him into a man fired with the dragon, yet not consumed by the flame. His dragon serves him, not vice versa.

Treatment: The Alchemical Lens

So we come to the crux of treatment: how do we proceed? Do we simply attempt to help the veterans adjust to civilian society? Or do we help to bring out the latent qualities that have been brought to the surface by the crucible of combat?

The process of alchemy involves a dissolving of veterans' ordinary perspectives, beliefs, and defenses. If combat is seen through the lens of an alchemist, it becomes a fertile ground for the discovery of a greater life. Therapists, other helpers, even family and friends can learn to serve this alchemy.

Perhaps the secret lies in an ancient alchemical caution, "Do not let the winged dragon escape from the flask." The condition of PTSD is an inability to integrate and express the reality of war. Therefore, instead of denying, avoiding, and negating the experiences of combat, veterans can be helped to use the power of the horror to transform and transcend their regular egocentric desires, such as selfishness and hate.

While most veterans will agree that combat changed them, they will also assert that those changes were primarily detrimental to their lives and have interfered in their civilian activities. That is to say, they have released the dragon, and it is now their master. The more they try to avoid and deny their torments, the more those memories of bloody chaos become stronger.

The theme of this book is that *combat has the power to transform and elevate the individual.* Helping veterans adjust to civilian life is important and admirable work, but it is a limited perspective. Veterans can become an inspiring and uplifting force in our country. The archetypes of the warrior/priest, the peaceful warrior, and the evolution of the soldier into the statesman are all examples of the transformable nature of trauma.

Military societies inadvertently maintain the belief systems of PTSD through the authoritarian nature of the military culture. Thus they keep soldiers from entering the civilian world, while also isolating them within the military as a soldier "with problems."

Veterans are dismayed by much of civilian culture, but probably most by the apparent lack of discipline and camaraderie among civilians. The more permissive nature of civilian life, such as lack of attention to detail, can contribute to the veteran's self-indulgence in the form of distractions. Ed, for example, was well trained in violence—and that training helped to keep him alive in Vietnam. But in the military there had been clear boundaries as to when that violence was acceptable. Civilian life, by contrast, does not provide the same opportunities for violent acts.

In Erich Fromm's brilliant book, *Escape From Freedom*,[2] he clearly demonstrated the difficulties that individuals struggle with when leaving authoritarian regimes and attempting to adapt to greater individual freedoms and corresponding responsibilities in dem-ocratic countries. When one has lived one's formative life under authoritarian dictators, the experience of responsibility in a free society is not an easy task.

A veteran named Sam told me that when he was discharged, he suddenly felt "empty." He wandered without direction for months while he tried to re-member what it meant to have the responsibility for his life.

Just as it is difficult to change from living in a dictatorship to living in a democracy, so it is difficult to change from military to civilian life. In civilian life, veterans—now perceiving life through different be-liefs—are confronted with social/organizational rules that seem nonsensical in light of the lessons they learned in combat. These lessons are never forgotten.

Veterans tell me of never taking the same route to and from work. "You never know about snipers, IEDs (improvised explosive devices), ambushes, booby

---

2 Fromm, Erich, *Escape from Freedom* (New York: Macmillan, 1994),

traps, and all of the other dangers that kill the person of habit." These are thoughts that civilians never have. As civilians, we never consider the possibility that someone is taking aim with our head in their sights.

Somewhere between the extremes of Ed (with his almost complete abnegation of ordinary life) and the politician (with his inspiring leadership and dedication to his beliefs) are those veterans who are able to appear quite successful and effective in their lives, yet still struggle with overwhelming symptoms.

When Symptoms Are Contained but Not Controlled

Sam was a professional before and after the war. His return to boardrooms seemed smooth, at first.

The boardroom was filled with a long polished wood table. Lining the walls were large floor to ceiling windows that did not open. Around the table were about thirty chairs. Each of the chairs had a person dressed in a dark suit with an ashen face.

Sam stood at one end of the table with his report in his hand. He had been hired to perform an examination of the company and decide how to improve the profit margin. In plain English, that meant deciding whom to fire. As Sam began to read his list of positions to eliminate, he felt the level of anguish in the room rise to a severe state. Suddenly one of the men gasped and fell out of his chair. Sam dropped his report and rushed to the man's side.

He removed the man's tie and saw that the man wasn't breathing. Sam knew CPR and began closed chest heart massage, alternating with mouth-to-mouth breathing. Sam was completely unaware of anything else in the room except for this man. Then other images began to intrude.

His point man was the first casualty when the Viet Cong ambushed his squad along the narrow jungle trail. The VC did their damage, then quickly retreated under the withering firepower of the Americans. Sam had rushed to his friend just as he had rushed to this man. Now Sam saw the sucking chest wound of his friend, he smelled the stench of battle, and he was flooded with the grief and terror of that moment.

Then he felt hands on him as the emergency technicians pulled him away and placed a resuscitator on the man. Sam came back to the room and calmly returned to the head of the table.

He picked up his report and waited for the ambulance technicians to remove the man on the stretcher. Then as the rest of the company, shaken, and shocked, reassembled. Sam completed his report.

That evening, at home, Sam was fixing himself a late-night snack. As he raised his head from the counter, he bumped his head against an open cupboard door. Rage overwhelmed him. He ripped the door off its hinges. He began to attack the cupboards in a fury. With his bare hands he smashed the doors and splintered the cabinets. His violence exploded from him in a dark red blackness, a complete loss of control, a murderous attack.

When he had completely demolished the cabinets he stopped, stunned at his destruction. Then he slumped to the floor and began to sob. He cried deep and inconsolably. His grief matched his previous rage in its intensity. Suddenly he was being held, as his wife and children crowded around him.

Sam is different from Ed. Sam is able to be successful in the ways that American society measures success—financially and in relationships. But Sam maintains control only through constant vigilance. He knows that something as basically innocuous as bumps on the head can release his dragon. His dragon is contained but not controlled.

Combat PTSD involves many complex factors that interact with the traumatic episode(s), such as:

* type of military training (boot, basic, Ranger, Special Forces, SEAL, Airborne, etc.)

* troop camaraderie,

* types of weapons used (automatic weapons, artillery, mortars, mines, remote controlled explosives, suicide bombers, etc.),

* event locations (jungle, city streets, open fields, etc.),

* expected vs. unexpected attacks (battles, ambushes, snipers, etc.),

* being constantly alert,

* having the job of killing people,

* enjoying the job of killing people,

* being constantly afraid,

* having little to no control regarding your personal decisions, and feeling guilty for having survived.

But the soldier's training for going into combat does not include preparation for the *emotional experiences* of and responses to combat, such as grief, anger, and despair. And when soldiers are discharged, they are given little to no preparation for the even greater emotional difficulties they are about to face. Typically, according to many veterans' accounts of their pre-discharge briefings, a sergeant reads a list of symptoms to the group and asks if anyone is experiencing those issues. It should be easy to imagine the soldiers' reluctance to raise their hand in that setting. Besides the potential loss of peer status that an admission of emotional suffering would entail, there would also be a delay in being discharged. One poor veteran told me that he actually raised his hand because he was troubled by his emotional difficulties. He was taken into one of the side rooms, where a sergeant yelled at him for delaying the discharge process. Needless to say, the soldier quickly recanted his complaints.

Chapter Two
Treatment and Spirituality

Suggestions and Guidance for Therapists

When we start to address bringing the spiritual into treatment, we need to recognize that we are in the presence of a Mystery. How individuals in therapy respond to these transformative spiritual energies and potentially transcendent vistas will depend in large part on how well they are able to participate in their treatment.

So before we get into the mystery of it all, I have to make some ground rules about treatment. Treatment of combat PTSD requires that veterans:

1. learn improved coping skills,

2. be made aware of the course of treatment,

3. set treatment goals,

4. be physically able to complete the treatment,

5. are not suicidal/homicidal, and

6. are not also struggling with more severe psychological disturbances (e.g., psychosis or a personality disorder).

In this chapter as well as the coming chapters, veterans' use of the exercises that will be suggested should be based on the therapist's clinical judgment.

This kind of treatment is a powerful approach that needs to be done slowly and carefully. When it is combined with spiritual exercises, veterans may eventually experience sudden insights and enormous relief from years of regrets, despair, and depression. But first there may be an increase in the severity of their symptoms, struggles with difficult emotions, and possible angry outbursts.

As I have already suggested, most treatment for combat PTSD does not make use of veterans' traumas to improve their lives, but instead focuses on adjustment to civilian life. The treatment presented here uses spiritual teachings to open up traumatized belief systems to greater perspectives.

What Is Spirituality?

The term "spirituality" is used here to represent the expression and desire of all individuals to fully live the human experience in terms of their highest ideals.

In this view, spirituality does not necessarily have anything to do with religion. It is quite possible that an atheist might be very spiritual, that someone uninformed in any particular religious belief system might have found spiritual dimensions in their life; that the scientist working diligently in well-defined research might be among the most spiritual, or that businesspeople in their daily work might uphold the highest of spiritual ideals.

This view is completely in keeping with my experience of an unexpected visit and audience with the Dalai Lama, years ago. My friend Tom was the local anchorman on the daily televisions news program. He called me excitedly. "Hey, guess what?"

"I have no idea." I answered.

"I'm going to interview the Dalai Lama tomorrow," he said. Then he added, "Well, I'm not, but this professor from Santa Barbara City College is, and my team is going to record it. Do you want to come?"

His Holiness was in Santa Barbara to accept an award from a local organization and was staying at a nearby hotel on the beach. The interview was to take place at the hotel.

This meeting was a once-in-a-lifetime opportunity. I revered the Dalai Lama, and had an attraction to Tibetan Buddhism. "Of course," I said. "I'll come. And I'll bring along my son." He was ten at the time.

Yet I really made no plans in terms of questions or conversation. I didn't know whether I would even have a chance to ask any questions. But as a result of my concern about showing the utmost respect to the Dalai Lama, I instructed my young son in the etiquette of greeting His Holiness by pausing, putting one's hands in the prayer position, and bowing.

When we entered His Holiness' hotel room, he came forward to greet us with a large smile. I paused to try and greet him in what I believed was the proper manner, but he did away immediately with any formal protocol by seizing my hand with both of his while looking into my eyes with a wonderful friendliness. He did the same for my son and for everyone who entered the room.

There were a few chairs arranged in a circle in the small room and my son and I sat down. The news crew and the interviewer assembled themselves around a small sofa.

After His Holiness had greeted everyone, he came over and sat beside us. The interview went on for the better part of an hour and was mostly centered on His Holiness' Buddhist message and his relationship with the Chinese government. I was more aware of His Holiness' presence than of his words, and how much more accessible he seemed than his answers.

When the interview was finished, we rose to our feet and I said, "Your Holiness I have a question."

"Certainly," he answered and moved to stand beside me. He began to rub my back, up and down my spine. It was a gentle touch but firm. I was a little surprised but nevertheless very pleased that he would be so obviously caring.

"I am a psychologist and I work with men who were in the war." I said.

He nodded vigorously.

"What is the best way to help them?" I asked.

He stopped rubbing my back and came around to stand in front of me. He looked at me for a moment then turned to his translator and said several words in Tibetan.

He looked at me carefully and said, "There are two things. First of all they need to have some sort of spirituality. It doesn't matter what kind, just have some kind. Second they need to know there is a difference between killing and murder. They are soldiers and it is their duty to kill the enemy. It is what they have to do."

I was somewhat disappointed, as these were ideas I was familiar with. However, I did my best to cover my disappointment and looked at him with gratitude.

He looked at me intently and said, "But you know best."

I was completely stunned. He had penetrated right to the core of my resistance, and easily swept away any of my preconceived notions of argument. He came closer to me and forcefully grabbed my arm. Holding my left arm firmly, he put his face close to mine and emphatically said, "No! You know best!" Then he put my hands between his into the prayer position.

I will always remember his great smiling face as I felt his wonderful compassion and kindness.

Penetration and Dissolution: The Mystical Crucible

The penetration of my own resistance by His Holiness helped me to see how much veterans need a similar kind of spiritual awakening and kindness from their therapists, so that they can go through the alchemical process they need to go through. In all survivors of trauma, especially combat veterans, there is a demand for an honest, authentic, and profound description of life. Veterans' belief systems have been shattered by the trauma; the old ideas no longer work.

In alchemy, this shattering is termed the *solve*. It is the dissolving of an idea, the changing of a self-concept. In the solve, veterans are suddenly open, questioning, and alone.

Come to the mystic, then, and sit with him when you are tired of all these other remedies that you have employed in vain; come and take a glass of wine with him. The mystic wine is the inner absorption, which removes all the worries and anxieties and troubles and cares of

*the physical and mental plane. All these are done away
with forever. It is the mystic who is at rest. It is he who
experiences that happiness which others do not experience. It is he who teaches the way to attain that peace
and happiness which are the original heritage of man's
soul.*[1]

Hazrat Inayat Khan

Mysticism is so widely misunderstood that it would
take another book to put into words what can't be put
into words. So for the purposes of this book, mysticism
is the term used to represent the process of discovering
our purpose in our manifestation.

The basic principle of alchemy is the mystical principle that: *all things come from One.* If all things come
from One, then anything may be made into anything.

The true alchemy is not the attempt to turn lead
into gold; that is a common misconception. Rather, it
is the transformation of the human personality from
an impure, selfish state, directed by constant desires
and greed, into a pure state epitomized by kindness,
patience, love, and a desire only to serve the One.

Alchemy is one of the ancient metaphors of mysticism. In mystical terms, alchemy represents the
transformation of the ego from a solid, selfish state
to an open, compassionate process. The ancient alchemical statement of *solve et coagule* (dissolve and
reform) suggests the possibility that changes in ego
structure can occur through a traumatic experience.
My own approach to treatment of combat trauma,

---

1 Inayat Khan, *The Complete Works of Pir-O-Murshid Hazrat
Inayat Khan* series (New Lebanon: Omega Publications and
Nekbkaht Foundation, 1996.)

therefore, uses not only well-established treatment modalities, but also mystical practices and the metaphor of alchemy.

There are many different mystical schools that teach a variety of mystical practices. One of those schools is the ancient school of Sufism (*tasawwuf,* in Arabic). The Sufis trace their lineage back through the Greek mystery schools, the Magi who visited Christ, the rishis along the Ganges, and all mystical lineages.

Sufism has made a detailed study of the ego, and has described its structure in terms of dynamic, interactive building blocks known as *nafs* (from the Arabic *nafas,* meaning breath). The type of nafs that are most present represents a person's level of evolution.

So, one lens through which to view PTSD is that when a veteran is overwhelmed by memories and consumed by personal issues, a particular level of nafs is functioning. And when a veteran is coping with the torment of memories through volunteering with the homeless and focusing more on others' dilemmas, another level of nafs is functioning.

The veteran's combat-shattered sense of self may be best viewed as a disruption of the nafs as the basis of ordinary belief systems.

However, as this book has been saying, that disruption can either enable the transformation of the ego into a more open, compassionate process, or freeze the ego's development into personal despair, thus maintaining life in the "never world."

Nafs—as well as being the building blocks of the ego—are also the *possibility* of the ego. In the Sufi perspective, the ego is actually necessary. There are many levels of nafs that represent the evolution of the ego. As the personality is transformed, the ego evolves.

Posttraumatic Growth (PTG)

It makes sense to say that Posttraumatic Growth (PTG) is the improvement of functioning in veterans after combat. But "improvement of functioning" is not so easy to define.

PTG depends on a subjective index, not an objective one. As Ronnie Janoff-Bullman points out in a recent article, "Growth involves internal changes—transformations within the person—rather than external changes in circumstances."[2] If, after struggling with traumatic memories, veterans are able to assert that because of their combat experiences they have a better life than they did before combat, then PTG has taken place. That assertion can be borne out by their improved sense of possibilities in their lives, and in their new understandings of who they are and how they might be in their world.

PTG has occurred when veterans can honestly look at the breadth of their experiences and say, "I can see now that the way things happened was necessary, and I feel like I understand more about life."

One Vietnam veteran, a Marine, said at the end of treatment, "I feel grief for everyone who suffered, including the enemy. They were people fighting for what they believed in, just as I was fighting for what

---

2 Calhoun, Lawrence G. and R. G, Tedeschi, *Handbook of Posttraumatic Growth: Research and Practice* (Charlotte: Lawrence Erlbaum Associates, 2006).

I believed in. It was my job, it was their job. It was tragic, but it was necessary."

A young veteran from the Iraq war said, "The politics don't matter. All that matters is that we try to keep it from happening again. But if we are attacked, or if some bully tries to murder another nation, we have to intervene. I think I learned a lot from my tours, but I don't want that war to be my defining point. I don't want to be only known as a veteran. I don't know if the war was necessary or not but I don't think that matters."

A Vietnam veteran who was a Long Range Patrol (LRP) specialist told me, "You know, I used to hate the government for lying to us. I used to hate the stupidity of officers. They got people killed. I still don't think that was OK, but I don't hate them any more. They had been put into a situation, and they didn't know enough. We called them, "shake and bake." Some of those guys are probably much worse off than I ever was. The government took advantage of us; we were young and idealistic. But governments do that, that's how they wage war. Now I know to always question what is told to me by the government and to recognize its need to maintain itself."

PART II
PREPARING FOR THERAPY
SESSIONS WITH VETERANS

The Rifleman's Prayer:
"Universe 6, Universe 6.[1] What the fuck? Over."
J. C. Muir

---

1 6 is the radio code for "Who is in charge?"

Chapter One
Prayer in the Therapeutic Setting
The Dialogue Between Limitation and Perfection

I believe that the proper utilization of time is this: If you can, serve other people, other sentient beings. If not, at least refrain from harming them. I think that is the whole basis of my philosophy.[1]

His Holiness the Dalai Lama

Frank and Ernest were arguing. They made a lot of noise but never solved anything. Finally Frank said, "Let's ask God." Ernest nodded his assent. Frank asked, "God are You listening?" There was a pause and then a patient but powerful voice said, "Yes Frank, I'm listening." Frank swallowed and said, "God is it true that a million years for us is but a second for You?" God's voice was clear, "Yes Frank, that is true." Frank, now emboldened by this success, ventured further, "God, is it also true that a million dollars for us is just a few cents to You?" God's voice sounded almost suspicious as He replied, "Yes Frank, that also is true."

Now Frank could hardly contain himself as he asked God, "Well God would you give us a million dollars?"

God's voice rang clear, "Yes Frank, in just a second."[2]

---

1 Dalai Lama, *An Open Heart: Practicing Compassion In Everyday Life*, (New York: Little, Brown, and Company, 2001).
2 Itinerant Dervish story as told by Merlin Krueger.

Prayer is not an easy topic for most therapists. The word produces religious images of kneeling in a church/temple/mosque, and is not part of treatment for most approaches. But prayer is the basis of alchemy.

God doesn't need our prayers, *we* do. Prayer allows us to forget our narrow self-concepts and move beyond our mind's chatter. The mystical prayer is the complete forgetting of the self and the discovery of Self. Regular prayer produces a different sort of energy in a person. Prayer is an active process to increase awareness of what is beyond the ordinary.

Sufis talk about the energy produced by prayer as one of the different types of *magnetism*, that sort of energy that both attracts and repels. For example, we may experience being very physically attracted to someone. That person has a *physical magnetism*. They may have an attractive physical body or practice physical exercise or eat a very balanced diet.

We may be attracted to someone who seems very intelligent and has a great deal of *mental magnetism*— someone whose world is one of the mind and is a very clear thinker. Such a person sees the world of thought as the world of life.

There may be someone we know who is very loving and has a wonderful *heart magnetism*. These are people who rarely talk about themselves, but instead are genuinely concerned about others. This does not mean that they do not consider themselves as important, but that they have discovered the joy of caring and service.

Then there are those few who exude a refined and subtle energy of the soul—a *soul magnetism*. Many times this person is not someone who has an exalted position within a religion, but rather who has gone through the "dark night of the soul," and emerged filled with light. Our own soul emerges in response to this person, and awakens from its sleep.

Prayer develops all these types of magnetism and gives an inspired energy to a space. We find the spaces where people pray regularly to be filled with a quiet and inspiring effulgence. Perhaps a peaceful, accepting atmosphere in a treatment environment (or any environment where you are present with a veteran) might help to quiet the chaos of the veteran's emotional structure.

If the term "prayer" does not appeal to you, think of it as simply moving from the ego into a less confined awareness. The process of helping veterans use their traumatic experiences to expand belief systems is improved when therapists are aware of both their own limited beliefs and their transcendent reality. This is not to say that therapists must be mystics, but prayer—along with an appreciation of art, poetry, and theater—aids in ameliorating veterans' anguish.

The arts are ways we have of ignoring our mind's daily chatter. For a while, through the arts, we are taken away from our linear pursuits and regular obsessions. When we are entertained by the theater we are moved into another world. When we are confronted by a powerful work of art our minds are suddenly shown other possibilities. And, of course, poetry is a way of saying something that can't be said.

> *Drinking wine with you, getting warmer and warmer,*
> *I think why not trade in this overcoat*
> *made of leaves and dirt?*
> *Then I look out the window.*
> *For what? Both worlds are here.*[3]
>
> Jalal ad-Din Rumi

If we, as therapists, are able to bring this atmosphere, it will affect the veterans who are asking us for help.

Preparing for the First Therapy Session

The first therapy meeting generally sets the tone for treatment of veterans. It is important to remember that veterans are a different population from most other patients. They are not the "worried well," looking for improvement in quality of life issues. Veterans have experienced repeated traumas of killing and having friends killed. Veterans have lived, sometimes for years, in regions where at any moment they could be killed. It is difficult for us as civilians to imagine what this does to the human psyche.

A degree of rapport can be established in the basic manner of asking questions, demonstrating empathy, being genuine, nonjudgmental, maintaining eye contact, and hearing (as different from listening). These therapeutic skills may be deepened and improved with two bits of information.

---

3 Moyne, John and Colman Barks, *Open Secret: Versions of Rumi* (Putney: Threshold Books, 1984), Quatrain 1243.

1. **Respect veterans' investment in their military service.** It is important that therapists are aware that veterans' politics are secondary to their need to have done a good job. It is essential to veterans that they were careful, courageous, and responsible, and that they made a minimal amount of mistakes during their tour. In their job, it was of prime importance that they watched out for themselves and their fellow soldiers as well as perform at their best.

The job of soldiering frequently requires very complicated moral decisions, and those decisions must be made very quickly; there is not the luxury of contemplation while other options are considered. Death, as a consequence of a decision, can be sudden and doesn't leave room for excuses.

For example, the child approaching, who seems to be carrying something behind her (possibly a grenade), and won't halt. What do you do? You may be willing to die rather than kill a child, but the other soldiers standing around you might have other wishes.

The first obligation for veterans was always to their fellow soldiers, regardless of the danger to civilian women and children. In civilian life, veterans pay the price of intrusive and invasive guilt regarding their actions in those situations. Veterans need to know that therapists understand these things: that when they killed civilians, veterans were doing their job as best they could.

2. The second and related point is to **never allow your own judgmental feelings to intrude.** It is impossible for us to fully understand the forces and dangers that soldiers face every day. We are not the

moral police, and while much of what we hear may be disturbing, we must maintain our empathic listening approach.

The process of establishing and maintaining rapport is enhanced by therapists' use of prayer. Forming an atmosphere of prayer can partially emerge from therapists' awareness of the sacredness of the therapeutic encounter. This awareness is facilitated by therapists' sense of the sacred in all relationships (children, wives, husbands, etc.). Prayer, in this sense, is an active presence in an atmosphere that is reverent, powerful, and wise. It means that we therapists are aware of the immanence, the presence, of the sacred in the world.

However, this sacred awareness is difficult to maintain if therapists have not had experiences of the mystical prayer.

A person should be so absorbed in prayer
that he is no longer
aware of his own self.
There is nothing for him but the flow of Life;
All his thoughts are with God.
He who still knows how intensely he is praying
has not yet overcome the bonds of self.[4]

Unknown Hassidic master

Breath, Thoughts, and Prayer

One of the aspects of mystical prayer is training the breath to coordinate with thoughts.

4 Green, Arthur and Barry Holtz, *Your Word Is Fire: The Hasidic Masters on Contemplative Prayer*, (New York: Paulist Press,) 1977).

Try this exercise: As you inhale think "purity," and as you exhale think "light." Sit with your eyes closed, imagining a scene of purity: a snowy landscape, the ocean's surface—anything that evokes something unsullied by humans. Then, inhaling, hold the breath, turn your eyes up, and place the bottom of your tongue gently against the roof of your mouth (the soft palate). Exhale with an image of light coming from above, through the top (the crown) of your head, out through your eyes, and think the word "light." This is an excellent practice for the five to ten minutes we have between seeing patients.

Prayer Does Not Need to Obviously Look Like Praying

The use of prayer does not require kneeling on the floor with the veteran and performing a religious ceremony. In fact, I would strongly advise against any outward show of either prayer or religious orientation. The intent here is to increase therapists' intuitive awareness and promote an atmosphere of safety, understanding, and insight. The veteran does not have to have any part of this prayer, nor should there be any attempt by the therapist to proselytize regarding the use of prayer. Prayer is anything that takes up your sincere, whole-hearted attention as you seek to make contact with Something beyond the ego's usual self-referential awareness.

The stories of Layla and Majnun are stories of divine love. Layla, one day, walking through the courtyard, lost in her thoughts of her beloved Majnun, unwittingly walked in front of a man praying. The man looked up angrily and berated her for committing such a sin. Layla apologized and then said, "I'm sorry, but I was thinking of my lover. Perhaps if you had been thinking of God you would not have noticed my transgression."

Any active gesture by therapists to be aware of experiences beyond the ordinary can be construed of as prayer. The key words are "beyond the ordinary." All traumas, by definition, are beyond the ordinary—and if therapists wish to be most effective, they need to remain open to the more esoteric possibilities of life. Prayer is an active process to increase awareness of what is beyond the ordinary. The Sufis assert that we do not pray for God but for ourselves. As such, prayer is important to the therapeutic process that has PTG as its focus.

Prayer can be conceived of as an essential ingredient in all human activities. It is our relationship to reality. In Sufi teachings, prayer is a dialogue between limitation (our concept of ourselves) and perfection (the ideal ego, God).

For the Sufi, the source of all of our anxieties is the gap between the immanent (the presence of God in the now) and the transcendent (the presence of God beyond the physical now). Prayer is the bridge over the gap. If prayer is practiced, then our lives become greater. Meditation is a form of prayer, saying the names of Allah is a form of prayer, breathing with the thought of God is a form of prayer.

The twelfth century Sufi master, Shahabuddin Suhawardi, was brought before a tribunal for not attending the daily prayers. He answered, "My life is a prayer." The mullahs were not impressed and had his head severed from his body.

If therapists actively pray, the atmosphere of prayer will be expressed in their attitudes. This is our purpose as therapists: first of all, to raise our own levels of awareness; to increase the development of our nafs (the components of the ego) into a greater understanding; and then help others to raise theirs. This atmosphere of prayer is not necessarily a passive atmosphere, but instead can promote power and action.

Types of Prayer

There are many kinds of prayer and many different ways of classifying prayer. The following are well known and are presented as ways of thinking about prayer.

Ceremonial Prayer. The ceremonial prayer, as experienced in the church, temple, mosque, and other places of religion, is the best known. This type usually employs the trappings of the particular religion and follows a definite structure, including a particular individual who has gained the recognition/certification as being someone qualified to lead this prayer.

Ritual Prayer. It is the ritual prayer that we are probably most familiar with. It may also be experienced primarily in a religious setting; however, it usually does not require a leader, and may be practiced by individuals privately. The ritual prayer usually involves a series of physical movements (prostration, hands in prayer position, etc.) that have significant esoteric meaning. If therapists are to create the atmosphere that will inspire trauma survivors, the practice of this ritual prayer is very important.

Of course, just doing the practice doesn't mean that the prayer will create the atmosphere. True, the practice alone will help in therapists' attitudes and awareness; but what will deepen the process is when the practice is done with awareness of the communication with the divine. There is a moment in all prayer when our minds are (at least briefly) focused on our awareness of communing with something greater than our ordinary notion of ourselves. The longer that moment is extended, the more powerful is our prayer.

Spontaneous Prayer. Finally, there is the spontaneous prayer. When we see an accident, when we see someone feeling sad, when we see pain in an individual, when we see any kind of suffering and we spontaneously entreat God to intervene, we are truly praying. When we find ourselves expressing the spontaneous prayer we have begun the practice of prayer in our lives.

The atmosphere of prayer does not have to give an impression of religion. Instead, this atmosphere will convey impressions of trust, knowledge, power, light, and authenticity.

Dimensions of Prayer

There are five well-known dimensions of prayer. The Sufi master Pir Zia Inayat-Khan has made a study of those dimensions. He discusses them as: thanksgiving, repentance, supplication, invocation, and communion.

Thanksgiving Prayer. Thanksgiving prayer is the celebration we have for this life. In this mode, we approach prayer as an expression of joy. Usually we are thankful for some positive occurrence in our lives. Perhaps we have been able to forgive someone, or someone has forgiven us. A prayer of thanksgiving can also be a daily thanks for having been given the opportunity simply to exist.

If we are in touch with our sense of thankfulness, we may find that our ability to sense our patients' emotions increases and is more effective. A prayer of thanksgiving may involve working with the breath, such as breathing in while feeling gratitude, and exhaling while feeling an offering or a giving out.

In psychotherapy, we frequently pay close attention to patients' rhythm of breathing. This rhythm gives us an idea of their level of anxiety. When patients are censoring a thought, when they are frightening themselves with certain memories, their rhythm of breath is changed. Through our work with our own breath, we become more sensitive to our patients' breath and may be able to be more effective in sensing their emotions.

Repentance Prayer. A prayer of repentance brings us, as therapists, closer to veterans, as they frequently ask forgiveness for their actions. Remembering the emotions involved in repentance gives us a closer contact with the veterans' emotional lives.

The foolish continue to make the same mistakes. The wise make new ones.

Hazrat Inayat Khan

According to a beautiful Sufi teaching, the one who errs and sincerely repents attains a higher virtue than the one who never errs. Certainly, psychotherapy involves a form of confession, a request for forgiveness. Since many soldiers believe that their sins are unforgivable, their expression of guilt and despair are all the more important in this atmosphere of prayer. The ugliness of the killing and the torture may have fixated their nafs at a lower stage, in the chaos of separation. Any sense those veterans might gain that they can be released from their guilt improves their potential for PTG.

> *I lament my mistake, but I enjoy the divine compassion.*
> Hazrat Inayat Khan

Pir Zia tells the following story of repentance:

In a small village lived a great saint. He was the protector and guide for the village. He would spend every day caring for the less fortunate.

One morning, exhausted from his previous night's work with the sick, he almost slept in and missed the morning prayers. Fortunately a supernatural being came to awaken him. Amazingly, this being was no angel but was the Dark Lord himself.

The saint thanked the Devil but asked him, "Why would you of all beings awaken me for prayer?"

The Devil looked slightly bemused, as if he knew he was seemingly acting out of character. "Well, I knew that if you missed the prayers you would feel so badly that you would cry." Here the Devil looked disgusted, "One of your tears would have absolved the entire village of all of its sins, and we couldn't have that!"

Supplication Prayer. In our prayer of supplication, we request assistance. A Hassidic story tells of a young Hassid who was hesitant to pray for G-d's help. The Hassid believed that he would be imposing on G-d. His rebbe told him, "You are doing G-d's work, you can ask Him for help. Pray for help."

What is it we desire in our prayer of supplication? The Sufis say that if our desire is not fulfilled, it is because we do not know how to desire. In our prayer of supplication we ask for the fulfillment of our needs, whether it is to be more effective in our treatment or to improve our ways of being with others. If we are aware of our needs, we will more effectively help veterans become aware of what they need.

Veterans have many desires—mostly, to be free from anger and despair. You can help veterans to form their desire as a wish. Have them verbalize their wish. How can they organize themselves to accomplish this wish? How can they direct their will to overcome ambiguity, confusion, and pain to clarify the essence of their wish?

I asked Bert, a Vietnam vet, "Are you able to say what you want?"

He answered, "I want to have never gone to Vietnam. I want these memories to not be there. I want to not have nightmares and be angry all the time."

I interjected, "Is it possible to appreciate your experiences and honor your bravery?"

Bert looked disgusted. He shrugged, "My bravery? I was scared shitless. I saw parts of my friends blown all to shit. I killed all those fuckers and I still hate them. I hate myself for hating them. It was a dirty bloody business and the Vietnamese didn't even want us to do it."

In the ensuing silence, I could feel some idea of his futility and anger. I asked him, "How do you want to be? You have a better idea of how life can be than us civilians. How do you want to use that understanding?"

Bert looked pensive. "That would be good. If I could actually use that shit, it would be great."

I responded, "You know, there is a Buddhist story about how a good farmer composts the cow shit, and the bad farmer throws it away. This is true about the shit we encounter in life. They call it 'the manure of experience.'"

Bert laughed.

If you are a therapist you recognize that in Bert's laugh is a beginning of process. That process may provide Bert with a different approach to living with traumatic memories.

Invocation Prayer. A prayer of invocation is a request for the presence of greater forces. An invocation creates a reality of the abstract. The unseen are requested to become more present.

An invocation is a direct request for a spiritual process. Alchemically, the prayer of invocation is a request for the spiritualization of matter and the recognition of the materialization of spirit.

In making a prayer of invocation, it is helpful to feel in contact with a presence of the divine. The form it takes is not important. It could be Jesus, Buddha, Mohammed, Krishna, Abraham, or anyone whom we, as therapists, call on for assistance in times of need. Silently invoking a presence during the treatment session frequently charges the session with clarity and improved insight.

In war, veterans' experience is primarily one of boredom punctuated by moments of complete terror. In civilian life, veterans struggle with the boredom of existence without the periodic break of terror. During war, veterans become desensitized to emotions that are not filled with anxiety and adrenaline.

Veterans develop nostalgia for those adrenaline-filled moments and think of them as meaningful experiences. As a result of their need to experience highly charged emotions, they ride motorcycles, go hang gliding, get in fights, and act out in other life-threatening pursuits.

Communion Prayer. You can help veterans to think of their nostalgia for adrenaline-filled emotions as the desire for a more meaningful life. Prayer comes out of need. From this need for meaning may come a prayer that brings an epiphany, a reconnection with what is beyond the ordinary. Any thought or feeling of being connected with the universe is a form of communion.

There are many different translations of Jesus' words, as his language was probably Aramaic. For example, the statement, "Blessed are the meek for they shall inherit the earth" may be alternatively translated as, "When that which is rigid in me is made flexible, I come into contact with the universe." A prayer that touches on communion is touching that sense of flexibility within us.

Veterans suffer from their rigidity, yet experience life as too dangerous for them not to be vigilant. If relaxing is framed as decreasing response time to danger and increasing the variety of options to respond to threat, veterans may discover greater contact with others.

Bert was unemployed and lived off the small disability the VA provided. He had been struggling with complete exhaustion after each day. All day he carefully paid attention to everyone he encountered on the chance that they might be violent. At the end of the day he returned to his apartment, set his perimeter, and moved into the closet, where he fitfully slept. The closet door was set open just a crack so that he could scan the room if he was suddenly awakened. Relaxing was not an option.

"Maybe if you relaxed, you might respond faster if there was a threat," I suggested to him. "I mean that you are pretty good at sensing when there is a threat. So if you trusted yourself more, you might be able to be even better at responding in a threatening situation."

Bert looked skeptical. "You mean that if I was relaxed I would be better at responding?"

I replied, "I don't know. Is that possible?"

Bert said, "Maybe. I don't know if I can do that."

This atmosphere of prayer may not seem to have much observable effect on most veterans. Veterans are too overwhelmed by their memories, pain, anxieties, and guilt to pay much attention to anything other than possible danger. Their constant attempt to be alert, to be prepared, and to always have a weapon available is both exhausting for them and annoying for those in relationship with them. But even though the effect of prayer may be subtle and barely noticeable, prayer is a powerful adjunct to treatment.

Veterans Educate the Therapist

An important part of maintaining rapport is to note that veterans are very sensitive to ordinary civilian questions such as: "What was it like to kill somebody?" "Did you feel that your life was in danger?" "How could you have done that?" and so on. Veterans will quickly withdraw if those questions are posed to them.

The key is to have them educate us. If we weren't there, if we weren't in the military (and even if we were), veterans need to explain to us what it was like for them. Veterans feel one down; they are seeking help. By asking veterans to help us understand their experience, we are empowering them.

It is important to ask what certain terms mean. Veterans do not expect civilians to understand military terms that have not appeared in the popular press. However, it is also important to demonstrate our understanding of terms after an explanation has been given, as veterans will soon grow weary attempting to constantly explain why they feel the way they do. We need to hear their meaning—not just in their words, but also in their tone, their weariness, their avoidance, and their mistrust.

For example, in Vietnam there was the term REMF, indicating a "rear echelon motherfucker"—an obviously disparaged group that provided support for the soldiers in the field and was looked down on by the combat troops. In Iraq, these individuals were FOBBITS, meaning soldiers who never left the FOB (Forward Operating Base).

The younger veterans, from Iraq and Afghanistan, are different. They are new to this. They are overwhelmed by not understanding. PTSD always happened to "someone else." These young men and women think of themselves as too tough, too resilient, too well trained. PTSD catches them off guard. Veterans don't like to be caught off guard, they don't like having to be in your office. But they don't have a choice anymore.

These younger veterans are in the early stage of PTSD. In many ways the early stage is the most frightening, as veterans do not understand why these experiences are happening. Why do they experience overwhelming anxiety? Why do they always feel angry? Why are civilians so stupid?

However, the good news is that this early stage of PTSD is most amenable to treatment. Once PTSD becomes chronic, it is more difficult to ameliorate. With the younger veteran, it is possible to interrupt the development of the disorder.

Basic Stuff: "Why Are We Doing This?"

The well-known techniques of establishing and maintaining rapport are relevant to work with veterans.

1. **Maintain eye contact.** This is a Gestalt technique and essential to the process. Never take your eyes away from the veteran. They appreciate this, even though they may feel mildly uncomfortable. This eye contact is affirming and validating of their importance. It assures them that they have your attention.

2. **Gather the vital information**, in a professional yet empathic manner, regarding family, education, parents, jobs, substance abuse, health, medication, and brief military history, (i.e., branch of service, location of basic/boot, AIT, schools, deployments, places stationed, indications of trauma, and discharge).

3. **Explain the treatment plan.** There are many different types of treatments for PTSD. For veterans, the therapeutic process is a reliving of events filled with blood, body parts, cruelty, courage, cowardice, shame, guilt, self-sacrifice, and everything else that keeps them awake at night.

Ask your patient and yourself: "Why do you want to do this?" (meaning the psychotherapy). This is an important question.

That question reminds me of a mystical experience I once had. My wife and I were at a meeting of mystics, a convening of sacred energies. During a certain mystical practice, individuals were asked to express something that needed the healing help of divine energy. I said, "The American soldier." My wife, supplementing what I left out, said, "The Iraqi soldier." The *Pir*[5] heard the split and united it as "Heroic self-sacrifice."

As trauma therapists, we are ready to begin the difficult task of helping the combat veteran relive their nightmares. We help them express the most intimate details of their killing, their fear, their exulting, and all of the opposing contradictory forces that make up their experiences. There often is a uniting of our resistance to hearing the brutality, and soldiers' resistance to sharing what is most painful.

Burnout: "Welcome To Our World"

As therapists, we must take care of ourselves. Burnout is a common therapist ailment, but in trauma work it gets even crustier. Burnout is called "compassion fatigue" in trauma work, and goes hand in hand with vicarious traumatization. Both compassion fatigue and vicarious traumatization can combine with positive countertransference (a process of therapists reducing their objectivity to such a degree that they over-identify with veterans' experiences) to produce a very disabled trauma therapist.

---

5 Sufi spiritual director.

Compassion fatigue happens when therapists (as well as family members and other helpers) become exhausted paying attention to endless tales of violence and the details of violence. We may find ourselves becoming very angry at home, in our other relationships, with colleagues, with other drivers, and basically with anyone who may cross our path. We may begin to abuse substances, finding at least temporary relief in being high. We become a difficult person whom others avoid.

Vicarious traumatization is very similar to compassion fatigue. While it may be part of the forces that create the fatigue, vicarious traumatization is the result of allowing the details of the stories to cumulatively affect us to the point that we begin to develop the symptoms of PTSD. Nightmares, depression, and panic attacks are some of the symptoms of vicarious traumatization. When combat veterans look at you thoughtfully and say, "You're beginning to act like us," or "Welcome to our world," you know that you might be in trouble.

But **positive countertransference** is probably the most insidious issue that faces even a seasoned trauma therapist. I once heard John Wilson, a Vietnam veteran and well-known author, therapist, and researcher, who worked with refugees from several South American countries, explain countertransference. He had heard a particularly brutal story and he shared it one morning. "A woman came to see me. She and her young son had attempted to escape from El Salvador but had been captured by the government forces. After repeatedly raping her, they killed her young son in front of her, cut off his head, and used it as a soccer ball." Then John turned to us and said, "What you are feeling is countertransference. Women almost always feel sadness, and men feel anger."

Self-Protection. How do we protect ourselves from these disabling maladies? We can't allow these experiences to overwhelm us. We have to honor our needs. It is essential to our souls that we restore our awareness of light and love in the face of such evil. If we give in, we will eventually become ineffective as therapists, and an emotional morass as human beings.

Remember, we do not have PTSD! It is our patients who struggle with traumatic sequelae. At the same time, however, it is important to recognize that we are affected by the trauma narratives. To prevent and ameliorate these difficulties, supervision, individual therapy, and continued self-discovery are all extremely helpful. But the most important techniques are prayer and meditation. A creating of our own ideal ego (that idea we have of how we might be, if only we would be who we could be) is basic to preventing and curing trauma therapy burnout. That ideal ego gives us inspiration and hope.

Practice for Healing from Burnout.

Here is a well known Sufi practice for daily healing from burn-out. If possible, say an invocation, prior to doing the practice, requesting the presence of that Being you feel closest to spiritually.

The Four Elements—Earth, Water, Fire, Air

Stand before an open window or even outside in the early morning. Close your eyes. You are going to breathe in and out the following elements:

1. **Earth.** Breathe in very slowly through the nose and out through the nose. Be aware of the energy from the earth rising throughout your body as you inhale. Be aware of the difficult and angry energy leaving your body and going into the earth as you exhale. Do this five times.

2. **Water.** Breathe in very slowly through the nose and out through the just barely opened mouth. As you breathe in, in your mind's eye see the mist rising from a pond. As you exhale, see a dam made of branches and mud suddenly break open, enabling the stagnant water to run freely. Do this five times.

3. **Fire.** Breathe in very slowly through your just barely opened mouth. Exhale very slowly through your nose. As you inhale, send the breath to the base of your spine, where you can envision a smoldering coal that bursts into flame when the breath reaches it. As you exhale, transform the flame into light surrounding your body. Do this five times.

4. **Air.** Breathe in very slowly through the just barely opened mouth. Exhale very slowly through the just barely opened mouth. As you inhale, reach far out into the universe to contact what the Hindus call *prana* or the life force. As you exhale, move out into the great vastness of outer space. Imagine the great distances between the stars and find yourself there. Do this five times.

Now open your eyes and say a prayer. Here is a suggestion:

Prayer of Healing

Beloved Lord, Almighty God!
Through the rays of the sun,
Through the waves of the air,
Through the all-pervading life in space,
Purify and revivify me, and, I pray,
Heal my body, heart, and soul.
Amen[6]

---

6 Inayat Khan, Hazrat, *Nayaz.*

Chapter Two
The Goals of Treatment
Learn
Be Responsible
Visualize Safety
Reduce Hostility
How Do You Want the Future?

Who is and is not a good candidate for treatment? When veterans seek treatment for their struggles, it means they have not been able to manage on their own. They realize that they are not coping well with their anger, intrusive thoughts, depression, anxiety, etc., and they have decided that they need help.

The treatment I have found that works best may cause veterans to initially experience an increase in their struggles and their stress levels. This means that if veterans are going to tolerate the initial stage of treatment, they need to improve their coping skills.

However, there are also some individuals who are not good candidates for this type of treatment. For example, certain types of physical difficulties, such as heart disease, preclude this approach. In addition, other types of psychiatric diagnoses secondary to PTSD—such as psychoses and personality disorders—are not appropriate for this treatment.

However, substance abuse is amenable to this form of treatment, particularly if the substance abuse is tied to PTSD. When the PTSD is treated, the substance abuse will usually decrease as the PTSD decreases in severity.

Clinical judgment has to be used in each individual case. In trauma cases, it is important not to adopt a specific point of view. Let the specifics of each case guide both the establishment of rapport and the course of treatment.

Learning: "What a Relief!"

The more the veteran can learn about PTSD, the better.

Online. A very good website for PTSD is www. ncptsd.va.gov. This site is run by the National Center for PTSD in the Department of Veterans Affairs Palo Alto Medical Center. It provides a description of the symptoms, ways of coping, and the different treatment approaches.

From the Therapist. Frequently, education provided by an experienced trauma therapist allows the veteran to decrease their distress. Sometimes the diagnosis of PTSD, alone, is a great relief to the veteran. "Really? Posttraumatic Stress Disorder? What a relief. I thought I was crazy," is a frequent response.

Diet. Nutrition and exercise are both important, but veterans may disregard these sorts of coping strategies. Veterans may believe that the use of nutrition is sort of "silly," "not much good," or "doesn't have anything to do with how I feel." While the role of diet has been widely publicized, many veterans are not particularly interested in changing over from fast food.

In addition, diet is a very individual matter. What is right for one person is completely wrong for another.

Sometimes the most one can hope for is to steer the patient in the direction of an increased intake of fruits and vegetables.

Certainly the relationship between how our physical body feels and what we eat would seem to be a no-brainer. But when faced with overwhelming anxiety and severe depression, anything that makes a person feel good (hamburgers, ice cream, etc.), even if only for a few minutes, is desired. Most people don't really understand the relationship between how we feel later and what we eat now. In the military, veterans generally experienced serious food deprivation, from K-rations to C-rations to MREs (meals ready to eat). And the military is not known for its gourmet cuisine. Indulging in fast food is something of a rebound from veterans' food-deprivation experience.

Important strategies in teaching coping skills include general education, pamphlets on nutrition, discussion of feelings after eating certain foods, and listening carefully to veterans' needs.

Exercise. In line with this is some regular form of exercise. If therapists are going to suggest exercise to veterans, it helps if the therapists themselves are something of a model. Therefore, therapists might also want to do regular exercise; exercise is a great way to reduce burnout. Veterans experienced the physically demanding basic training, and many of them went on to experience even more physically rigorous advanced training in the Rangers or other specially trained teams. They understand what it means to exercise, as well as what it means to their mental conditioning.

However, they are not used to being self-starters. They are used to having a drill instructor or officer ordering them to do push-ups and other types of conditioning exercises. Their current tendency to ignore their bodies can be seen as further evidence of their adolescent-fixated rebellion against authority.

A primary symptom of combat PTSD is the complete lack of trust in authority. It is important to explore with veterans their need to decide for *themselves* regarding what they do with their body. Note that the older Vietnam veteran is frequently far removed from any kind of physical conditioning and should proceed very carefully.

In addition, many veterans have legitimate physical limitations in the form of disabilities. Some have shown great courage in the overcoming of those disabilities, but others will find every reason possible to avoid doing any physical exercise. Yet in addition to reluctance, these veterans may also express a need to exercise, and may acknowledge that the exercise would greatly benefit their emotional health. This latter group needs to be gently confronted with their excuses and encouraged to devise their own exercise plan, within the limits of their disability.

Some of the symptoms that will show an increase in the course of the treatment are anger, intrusive thoughts, anxiety, and nightmares.

Being Responsible for One's Feelings: Anger

"You make me so angry!" No one makes us feel. We choose how we feel. Other people may influence our choice, but we are responsible for our feelings.

77

When I accuse you by saying, "You are making me angry," I am giving up my power to you. I am making you responsible for my anger.

One of the worst questions a therapist can ask is, "How did that make you feel?" That question promotes the client's avoidance of responsibility for their feelings. Better questions include, "What was that like for you? How did you experience that? When that happened, what was happening for you? What was your experience?"

When I work with veterans, particularly in groups, I always attempt to explain this issue and why I never ask the "How did that make you feel?" question. I had been meeting with one group for over five years and had repeated this insight to them many times. At one point, the group surprised me with a very nice gift: a pocket watch with the Vietnam Memorial Statue on the cover and the Vietnam service ribbon on the base. On the back they had taken the time to engrave my name along with a question. The engraving read, "Larry, how does this make you feel?"

When I read the inscription, at first I felt like I had failed miserably. Then I looked up at the group. They were laughing and smiling. They got me on that one!

Hazrat Ali, the Prophet Muhammad's brother-in-law, was a fierce warrior. He pledged his life to the Prophet and the Message.

Sometimes the opposition to the Prophet would bring armed conflict.

In one of the many battles, the Prophet and his followers were forced to fight, Hazrat Ali, was in savage hand-to-hand combat. Hazrat Ali was a skilled warrior and had overcome his foe by pinning him to the ground.

As Hazrat Ali raised his sword to deliver the killing blow the enemy soldier spat in Hazrat Ali's face. The master suddenly lowered his sword and stood up, allowing the enemy to survive. The enemy warrior stood up in amazement and said, "But you should have killed me! I even spat on you. Why do you spare me?" The master spoke in an even tone, "You angered me with your insulting act. I cannot act in anger, Allah forbids it."

Joe had been in many firefights and had witnessed many dead and wounded in Vietnam. When he came back, his anger was so great that he was jailed twice for assault. He came in for therapy because he was frightened that his third strike would land him in prison.

I asked him, "What happens? How do you become so violent?"

He shrugged and said, "I just see red, and it's all over."

"You mean you can't stop yourself?" I asked.

Joe looked angry and said "Yes! Nobody believes me but it's true. I can't stop!"

I thought for a second and said, "How about when you say this to a judge? Does he believe you?"

Joe looked very pissed off, got up, and walked out of the session. I never saw him again.

Only human beings can judge and reason; we understand consequences and think in the long term. It is also true that human beings can develop infinite love, whereas to the best of our knowledge animals can have only limited forms of affection and love. However, when humans become angry, all of this potential is lost. No enemy armed with mere weapons can undo these qualities, but anger can. It is the destroyer.[1]

His Holiness, the Dalai Lama

I sometimes ask veterans to rate their anger from one to ten, with one being at complete peace, and ten being murderous, out-of-control rage. Most veterans say that their anger is generally about a three or four, but that they can go to a ten in a flash. That is never true. If you can go to ten in a flash, that means that you are probably already at a seven or eight.

His Holiness, the Dalai Lama states:

When people get angry they lose all sense of happiness. Even if they are good-looking and normally peaceful their faces turn livid and ugly. Anger upsets their physical wellbeing and disturbs their rest; it destroys their appetites and makes them age prematurely. Happiness, peace, and sleep evade them, and they no longer appreciate people who have helped them and deserve their trust and gratitude.[2]

Anger is probably the most difficult of all veterans' emotions. The main difficulty in treating it is that anger has been a valuable tool for veterans. They were trained to deal with their fear by getting angry and killing the enemy. Anger kept the veteran alive in combat. Some veterans cannot imagine what it would be like not to feel angry most of the time. After about

---

1 Dalai Lama, *How to Expand Love: Widening the Circle of Loving Relationships*, (New York: Simon and Schuster, 2006), 3.
2 Dalai Lama, *The Path to Tranquility: Daily Wisdom* (New York: Compass, 2002).

a year of treatment, one veteran told me, "I woke up this morning and I felt like I had lost one of my friends. I wasn't angry."

It's essential to realize that *an expression of anger is an expression of a need, and all needs are a form of prayer.* We experience something lacking, a longing for something (e.g., peace, happiness, love). Someone says or does something that exacerbates that need (seemingly keeps us from experiencing peace), and we feel angry. We have forgotten, or never recognized, the origin of our anger as a prayer to fulfill a need.

Anger also stops stress by discharging high arousal levels, from feelings of anxiety, hurt, guilt, frustration, and threats to either our self-concept or to our physical safety. In this way, anger is a coping response to increased stress. Treatment of PTSD frequently increases stress. The increase of stress will cause an increase in anger. Therefore, if we want veterans to survive treatment, it is essential to teach anger-coping responses.

Sometimes veterans label their physiological state as anger, when it is really a rekindling of adrenaline. Veterans are trained to overcome fear (an adrenaline experience) through anger. Certainly, adrenaline is at high levels in the bodily system during combat, and actually, for much of the time during soldiers' tours of duty. When the adrenaline of combat was in full sway, soldiers were able to kill the enemy. Veterans often tell the stories of how they were unable to stop shaking after the battle, as the adrenaline slowly subsided. When the adrenaline is restimulated, veterans experience this force as anger.

81

Many types of cathartic therapies are based on the expression of anger. These therapeutic modalities help individuals come to terms with their anger regarding their possible mistreatments and their traumas. However, *the method of catharsis is a very dangerous approach with veterans*, as it can open up violent acting out. Most studies have supported the contention that cathartic therapies, instead of supplying a relief from anger, actually provide a rehearsal for future angry expression. The ventilation of anger tends to create a more permissive attitude towards the expression of anger and may even fixate angry attitudes.

Bringing anger under control must be based on a belief that control of anger is helpful. For example, Joe in the previous illustration did not believe that it was possible for him to control his anger, and blamed others for putting him "out of control."

Many veterans have been involved in domestic violence, gone through divorces, lost jobs, and possibly been in jail as a result of their poorly controlled anger. As a result of experiencing the consequences of their anger, these veterans may finally recognize the value of gaining control over it and be motivated to take responsibility.

Veterans' avoidance of anger control is based in some part on military training that encouraged violence within the troops. Although intersquad violence is officially prohibited, many drill instructors subtly encourage the use of anger and violence in the troops against each other as one of the ways of preparing them for combat.

Anger is also a very powerful means of controlling others that has been modeled by the drill instructor, the sergeant, and the lieutenant. Because of their role models, it is difficult for veterans to learn that in civilian life, the expression of anger is generally counterproductive.

The most important thing for veterans to learn is that regardless of what has triggered their anger, there is nothing inherently right or legitimate about it. Veterans' anger is an expression of their pain, and their suffering has to be brought into awareness if their anger is going to be reduced.

While it is normal to feel justified about our anger, it is more important to *question* that justification. The bumper sticker quote from Jiddhu Krishnamurti, "Question authority," is directed at questioning our own authority to believe that we are justified in our angry response.

The treatment for PTSD will bring suffering to the surface and increase stress. Coping responses such as self-talk, anger inoculation, rehearsing choosing responses other than anger, and improving the veteran's ability to more effectively communicate are important to have in place prior to beginning treatment.

Education. Education regarding the complexities of anger is an important first step. A good introduction to changing anger is to offer a handbook condensing several anger-management techniques. Books such as *When Anger Hurts*[3] are invaluable for the veteran. Unfortunately, many veterans are not well oriented to reading, and tend to ignore pamphlets and, especially, books.

---

3 Mackay, Matthew and Peter Rogers and Judith Mackay. *When Anger Hurts: Quieting the Storm Within.* (Oakland: New Harbinger Publications, 1989).

Anger Journals. A good beginning in learning to cope with anger involves assigning veterans "anger journals" that detail:

* date and time,

* a brief description of the event,

* a self-assessment of peak arousal and aggression,

* listing the pre-existing stressors (feeling threatened, difficulty at work, etc.),

* listing the trigger thoughts ("I am being blamed unfairly"), and

* describing the result of the anger (felt relief, excited, etc.). Unfortunately, this too has very low compliance results.

Getting Perspective. Taking responsibility for one's anger is challenging. Ways of developing this self-responsibility include learning to understand others' motivations; staying in touch with one's positive feelings for that other person; being aware of how one felt just prior to the trigger incident; exploring options to anger; alternative ways of reducing stress; and changing expectations.

Understanding the motivations of others. Understanding the other person's motivations is difficult for anyone, much less veterans. Very few of us want to stop in the midst of letting self-righteous anger build to ask ourselves why the other person is doing or saying whatever they are doing or saying, which we are using to allow ourselves to become angry. Underlying this reluctance may be the fear that if we question our basic justification by trying to see it from the other person's point of view, we might not be able to be angry. And then how are we going to stop our stress?

In my work with very embattled and entrenched couples, civilians as well as veterans, I frequently ask them why they stay with each other. A very common response is, "Because we love each other." My next question is, "What do you love about each other?" Their answers are usually a blank look or an attempt to change the subject. They simply don't have a way to express what's positive about the other person.

Helping veterans express positive feelings in words. In order to access our positive feelings, we need to be able to verbalize them. If we can't put our feelings into words when we are not actively angry, we probably won't be able to access them when we are in the throes of building towards anger.

In working with veterans to develop this important skill, ask them to do the following:

1. Be aware of those moments when you are not angry.

2. In those moments, allow yourself to feel positive emotions for the difficult people in your life. See if you can ignore your innumerable resentments and well-justified anger.

3. Experience an awareness of the qualities that attract you to those people. Can you articulate those emotions? How would you express your positive emotions to those people?

4. If expressing positive emotions feels too risky or difficult, ask veterans to "recognize the degree to which your resentments are blocking your ability to stop stress without having to become angry."

5. Try and remember how you were feeling prior to the incident that triggered your anger. Be aware of the gradual buildup of irritability, and the general feelings of failure, shame, guilt, and self-pity that usually precede anger.

6. Take responsibility for those feelings, and be aware of how those emotions contribute to your anger.

Of course, there are many additional ways to stop and discharge stress other than anger. However, veterans are not likely to use them if they have not been trained and educated in their use.

Alternatives to anger: exercise. The most common alternative to anger is exercise, but exercise has its limits and its restrictions (physical disability). In addition, exercise primarily distracts from the issues that are involved in the anger, and does not help in their solution.

Alternatives to anger: crying. Crying, as an alternative to anger, is also very common. However, it is threatening to veterans in terms of their self-concepts (e.g., "crying is weak"). In addition crying creates feelings of vulnerability that are anathema within the military. In the male military, in particular, men are less accepted in the enlisted ranks for showing any kind of emotion that might make them appear female.

Caveat: defer emotional expressions. During the early stages of helping veterans to improve coping skills, it is important that they not become too emotional. It is important to delay the emotional expression, even though veterans may have a significant amount of grief and need to have something of a catharsis. This is because if the emotional event occurs too early in the treatment, prior to establishing a trusting relationship with the therapist, veterans may feel humiliated and leave treatment.

Alternatives to anger: cleaning and organizing. Other ways of dealing with stress may involve cleaning and organizing one's living space. It is also true that cleaning and organizing do not focus on the underlying issues. Staying busy is usually a way of avoiding issues; but avoiding may be necessary until the level of stress goes down sufficiently for veterans to be able to cope effectively without becoming angry.

Alternatives to anger: problem-solving discussions. Problem-solving discussions are great if the veteran is able to do them without becoming angry.

The treatment for PTSD will bring suffering to the surface and increase stress. Coping responses such as self-talk, anger inoculation, rehearsing choosing responses other than anger, and improving the veteran's ability to more effectively communicate are important to have in place prior to beginning treatment.

Spiritual Assistance. If veterans are open to spiritual perspectives and have some sense of spiritual guides (i.e., angels), a reminder might be given that those guides become less available when veterans are angry (it is said that angels leave when we become angry). Have veterans choose a particular spiritual guide and put a reminder of that guide in their living spaces. Since Muslims are not allowed to have images of the prophet, perhaps prayer beads might suffice. Anything that reminds veterans of their spiritual connections can help them change their anger.

The Sufi master Pir Vilayat Inayat Khan used to say that anger is like the wind that blows over the ocean. We are the boat making use of the wind, and we decide where the wind takes us. Anger is energy, and how we use that energy is up to us. A boat will sometimes use the wind to go in a different direction than the wind's. We can use the energy of our anger to create improved relationships instead of increased animosity and more anger.

As an illustration, my wife has the capacity to stimulate my extreme emotions most easily, both positive and negative. Over the years of our marriage, we have had our dynamics (my euphemism for fighting). After one rather intense dynamic, I asked her if she would like to go out for a meal.

She looked at me in disgust and said, "Why do you want to go out? All we do is fight."

I thought for a second and replied, "Yes, but I love all of you. Not just the parts that are easy to get along with, but also the parts with which I have difficulty."

She looked even more disgusted and said, "That is such bullshit."

Which of course it was. However, I was using the energy of my anger to be creative, and that at least leads to different dynamics.

Intrusive Thoughts:
Na Koja Abad (The Land of No-Where)

Experiencing the sudden memory of a traumatic event is extremely disturbing and disconcerting to veterans. Their attention is essentially hijacked, completely drawn to the memory. The intrusion of internal images of blood, screaming, and body parts is so overwhelming that veterans feel helpless to stop the memory. And even after the intrusion passes, they are left shaky and fearful. They do not believe that anyone else can understand, and they have a fear of being insane. They may begin to abuse drugs and alcohol in an attempt to numb their emotional responses to these memories.

The intrusive thoughts can be viewed as the scattered nafs attempting to reform. This is illustrated in the famous Sufi poet Shahabuddin Suhawarardi's epic poem, "The Crimson Archangel," where the self attempts to find itself and ends up in the place it was before, but as a superior self. "Where are you from?" asks the pilgrim. "*Na Koja Abad*, [the land of no-where]," replies the Archangel. Veterans are the strangers who wish to return home from their never-land, the land of no-where. When they find themselves, they find the superior self.

Treatment for Intrusive Thoughts. Treatment, particularly in groups, increases the severity and frequency of intrusive thoughts. The veterans should have been prepared for this intrusion by previously experiencing long-term individual treatment. However, while the individual treatment allows veterans to become more comfortable with their traumatic memories, groups provide a stimulation beyond the individual experience. Hearing similar experiences from other combat veterans rekindles many memories that were not accessed in the individual sessions.

Once in therapy, veterans may be able to recognize the beginning of the intrusion, as many of them experience a sudden anxiety just before an intrusive thought arises. If they can anticipate the intrusion, then they can practice "grounding techniques" that help keep them in the here-and-now when traumatic memories become vivid.

Grounding techniques. There are several grounding techniques that, with practice, can make a difference in veterans' ability to cope successfully with intrusive thoughts.

1. **Safe memory.** A good grounding technique is the establishing of a "safe memory." A safe memory is a time in veterans' lives when they felt safe and protected. Usually, this time of safety is in childhood. However, many veterans are survivors of child abuse, and, for them, childhood was not a time of safety. In this case, they will need to find or create a safe memory from a later time.

2. It is important to keep working with veterans until they have reached an awareness of safety. They then can return to this safe awareness when they realize they are about to be overwhelmed by intrusive thoughts. Some veterans use the therapy office as their safe place and their memory of being safe.

3. **Visualizing protectors.** Visualizations of protectors (Jesus, Buddha, etc.) can be very useful. These can involve seeing the protector close by and surrounding themselves with light. If veterans are able to do practices that surround them with light in ordinary moments, they might be able to remember these practices during moments of distress.

4. **Anchoring breath.** A good grounding exercise for veterans is for them to imagine that when they inhale, their breath comes in through the top of their head and stops at their hips. Then, as they exhale, the

breath goes down through the center of their legs into the earth and wraps itself around a tree root. After practicing this for a while veterans will begin to feel much better. Then have them inhale and draw earth energy up through their legs and into their body. When they exhale, have them focus on any negative thoughts and energy, sending it out through the arms and giving it to the earth through the hands. This can also be done from the whole body—experiencing the negativity leaving and going into the earth through the exhalation.

Treatment for Anxiety: "The Pull of the Future is Stronger than the Push of the Past"[4]

PTSD is all about high-arousal states. From hyper-vigilance to poor concentration, the high arousal of PTSD is an interfering factor in veterans' lives.

One reason why veterans have a difficult time being in crowds (aside from the fear of not being able to control their environment) is the stimulus overload. The amount of stimulation in a crowd is too much for someone who is already very highly stimulated.

Veterans are unable to adequately concentrate unless they are oriented to a threat. They are able to completely focus attention for a prolonged period of time if they are anticipating an attack, listening for movement in a danger zone, or on the alert for possible threat.

However, if the object of concentration is not life threatening—perhaps work instructions, written orders, even a list of shopping items—veterans have

4 Pir Vilayat Inayat Khan.

difficulty paying attention. Most of them are used to a high-arousal state, and feel uncomfortable when that state is reduced. This partially explains symptoms such as the inability to fall asleep, high blood pressure, and irritability.

1. **Relaxation techniques.** Therapeutic treatment may initially increase the level of arousal, to the point where it may be uncomfortable. If veterans are already barely able to tolerate their current state of arousal, healing work needs to be done with relaxation exercises prior to beginning treatment. Relaxation techniques can include tensing muscles and then relaxing them.

2. It is necessary to know how tension feels in relation to relaxed so the contrast of tensing and relaxing is essential. Focusing the tensing and relaxing on specific muscle groups is necessary if veterans are to use this technique in their lives.

3. **Desensitization to trigger stimuli.** Veterans need to be familiar with the process of desensitization to trigger stimuli. They might want to write out lists of possible triggers (i.e., an anxiety list) and attach the subjective units of distress scale (SUDS) to each trigger. SUDS are a way of listing relative levels of anxiety produced by different trigger events.

4. **Going through the anxiety list.** After teaching veterans relaxation techniques, take them through the anxiety list (while they are relaxed) and help them reduce the SUDS for each one of the trigger stimuli.

The goal is not to completely remove all anxiety, but to reduce the severity of the anxiety to the point where it is manageable and tolerated. In teaching these coping skills, therapists must attend to veterans' sometimes very idiosyncratic perspectives regarding triggers. For example, with Vietnam veterans, the smell of diesel fuel is frequently a trigger. For Iraq veterans, it can be the sight of an unusual object beside the road. These sorts of stimuli are critical in the treatment, and must be confronted by veterans in learning the coping skills.

The Importance of Practice. It is important that veterans practice these exercises during ordinary moments. Otherwise, when the nightmares and other trigger stimuli produce agitation and panic attacks, this population will find it difficult to focus concentration on these exercises unless there has been rehearsal. Veterans will understand the necessity of rehearsal even more than their therapists.

Susan was particularly reluctant to practice the relaxation exercises. "I can't do this," she said with exasperation after I had begun helping her learn how to relax. She had been a nurse in Vietnam and struggled with her grief over all the lives she hadn't saved. Instead of honoring the memory of soldiers she had healed, she fixated on her perceived failures. As a result of her self-inflicted torment, she was constantly agitated, unable to find peace.

What happens? I asked."

"I have to talk. My mind won't be still. I told you that," she glared at me.

I asked her, "Is it possible that if you relax, you will forgive yourself and will let go of your need to punish yourself?"

"Why wouldn't I want to do that?" she angrily replied.

"Perhaps you might feel that you were once again letting those soldiers down," I ventured.

Susan looked a bit startled, and then said, "Maybe. I don't know. OK. Let's try again."

But nothing is that easy, and it took a while before she was able to find at least a semblance of peace.

If closing the eyes is difficult. The simple act of closing their eyes during a meditation may be a very difficult request for veterans. In asking them to do this, we are asking them to stop being fully alert and prepared. Remember: veterans' lives and the lives of others depended on their degree of alertness.

If they are unable to close their eyes, ask them to visualize the meditation with their eyes open. Then ask them to:

* Inhale through the nose and hold the breath for a few seconds.

* Exhale through the nose as fully as possible, expelling all the air out of the lungs.

* Relax and inhale deeply, into the abdomen, again holding the breath.

* Repeat this several times.

* Then breathe normally.

Generating Hope. Veterans are haunted by the past. Past experiences are intrusive and painful. Because of their traumas veterans lose their sense of hope, and sink into depression.

Abu l-Qasim al-Qushayri, an eleventh century Sufi, described hope as "the attachment of the heart to something loved that may occur in the future. Just as fear falls upon future time, so hope arises because of something to which one looks forward."[5] Pir Vilayat Inayat Khan said, "The pull of the future is stronger than the push of the past."

Traumatized veterans have little hope for the future. They have only the fear that past traumas will repeat, and the absolute necessity to be completely ready if those traumas should reoccur (and veterans are convinced that they will).

Adjusting perspectives. Sports metaphors work well in helping veterans adjust their perspectives. In a football game, it is not the previous play that is important. What is important is what will be the score at the end of the game. The desired score at the end has a greater influence on the game than the play that was just run. In other words, the future has a greater influence on the present than does the past.

It is true that the present is the result of the past, and the future is the result of the present. Buddhism, for example, teaches us to be in the present, for both the past and the future are contained in the present. For veterans, however, the present is consumed by the past, through memories, fears, and anxieties. The future thus is filled with uncertainty and dangerous possibilities.

In a state of hopefulness, all of us hope that what we hope for will become real; in a state of fear, we hope that what we fear will not become real. Yet hope is contained even in the anxiety regarding what we fear. We can help veterans' hope within the fear become more present by supporting their vigilance. If they

---

5 Dalai Lama and Howard Cutler, *The Art of Happiness*, (New York: Riverhead Books, 1998).

can accept that they are being as alert as possible, then they can hope that what they fear will not occur.

Resistance. Veterans will actively resist this insight about hope, because it is a genuine inroad to their years of struggle with anxiety and fear.

The honey of life is hope. If the knowledge of God does not give hope to attain the divine bliss which is attained in life, that knowledge is of no use.[6]

Hazrat Inayat Khan

Nightmares: Lowering Hostility

He who stores evil in his heart cannot see beauty, because there is no good in this world that has not a little spark of evil in it. [7]

Hazrat Inayat Khan

John was a Vietnam veteran who was consumed by feelings of guilt. Because of these guilt feelings, he was unable to let himself feel positive about other people. He was sure that most people would condemn him if they knew what he had done in the war. John hated all the Vietnamese: the Viet Cong had tortured and mutilated the body of his friend, and the ARVNs (South Vietnamese Army) had deserted when firefights had begun, and had stolen some of his personal things. John also hated most civilians for their ignorance and their lack of understanding for his feelings.

---

6 Inayat Khan, *Complete Works of Pir-O-Murshid Hazrat Inayat Khan: Original Texts: Lectures On Sufism, 1923 II: July-December* (London, The Hague: East-West Publications, 1988).
7 Ibid.

Nights, for John, were filled with sweat and loud noises. Nightmares were constant, involving horrific images and feelings of imminent death. He thrashed about in his sleep, yelling and kicking. He had been divorced twice, and his third wife now slept in another room.

Love, compassion, and concern for others are real sources of happiness. With these in abundance, you will not be disturbed by even the most uncomfortable circumstances.

If you nurse hatred, however, you will not be happy even in the lap of luxury. Thus, if we really want happiness, we must widen the sphere of love. This is both religious thinking and basic common sense.[8]

His Holiness, the Dalai Lama

John's feelings towards other people were very complex. On one hand, he experienced genuine sympathy and concern for the innocent and the underdog. But he felt nothing but anger for the well-to-do and the successful. His daily fantasies were violent, directed towards people who seemed happy and content. Inwardly, he wanted to show everyone his reality—something that he saw every day in his intrusive thoughts—that people are nothing more than "sacks of blood."

Love is the essence of all religion, mysticism, and philosophy.[9]

Hazrat Inayat Khan

---

8 Dalai Lama, *How to Expand Love: Widening the Circle of Loving Relationships* (New York: Simon and Schuster, 2006), 2.
9 Inayat Khan, *Complete Works of Pir-O-Murshid Hazrat Inayat Khan: Original Texts: Lectures On Sufism, 1923 II: July-December* (London, The Hague: East-West Publications, 1988).

The Torment of Constant Nightmares. Think of trying to go to sleep knowing that you will be confronted with the images and emotions of your most horrible experiences. Even if you drink yourself to sleep, smoke marijuana until you pass out, or take sleeping medications that reduce your alertness during the day, you still must struggle with your traumas every night. At a time when you need to rest your mind and body, you are not given any respite. Veterans are tormented about their actions in war both day and night.

Nightmares are one of the most common symptoms of PTSD, many times the most disturbing. On the most basic level, they keep veterans from getting adequate rest. A typical experience may be sleeping for only a few hours, waking from an intense dream, sweating, getting up, checking the house (the "perimeter"), trying to go back to sleep, having another nightmare, and so on throughout the night. In many ways, it is no wonder that veterans are easily angered. They have built up a considerable sleep debt.

Treatments. While there are many sleep medications that apparently have a significant impact on the frequency and severity of nightmares, there also are other, non-medicated alternatives.

Working consciously with dreams. It's possible to work therapeutically with veterans to bring their nightmares under conscious control.

✳ Ask veterans to try to remember their nightmare when they awaken from it.

✳ Then ask them: "What happened? Who was there? How did you feel? What was most terrifying about the dream?"

✳ Have the veterans write down a description of the nightmare, bring in their transcript into the treatment session, and read the dream out loud.

✳ Ask them to read the transcript before they go to sleep at night.

✳If they are in a group, have them read the transcript to the group and discuss it.

This next part is where the possibility of hope and transformation comes in. Encourage veterans to return to the dream when they are able to return to sleep. *But have them try and create a different ending, attain some control over the events, and use whatever helps them feel a sense of support and strength.*

They may want to have someone else in the dream with them who is powerful and supportive. A powerful spiritual force can be extremely helpful. Have them create an ending that is a self-enhancing experience.

Instead of a dream ending with veterans waking up in terror, help them work towards making friends with the shadow dream figures. During the day have the veterans focus on those shadows (i.e., Vietnamese, Iraqis, Afghanis) with positive thoughts, seeing the former enemy as a new friend.

Therapy involving art, music, dialogue, and dream interpretation. Working with art, music, dialogue, and dream interpretation can give veterans excellent coping skills for dealing with increased nightmares as the treatment progresses.

Art. The use of art is a valuable addition to the therapeutic process. Veterans may be reticent to begin because of how they perceive their artistic ability, but their desire to reduce their nightmares usually overcomes that reticence. Have them draw the images in their nightmares: the dead bodies, the enemy, even their fear and their dread. Encourage them to use whatever media they want. Then encourage them to discuss the images and their emotions for some time.

Dream dialogue. Help veterans develop a dialogue with the dream images. Use the empty chair routine, in which veterans put their former enemies in the chair, and have veterans discuss their issues with the images in the chair. Help them give a voice to the images.

Music. Music will become an important part of treatment, once music therapy is used for psychological healing. Playing inspiring music prior to sleep may eventually have some impact on reducing the frequency of veterans' nightmares.

Inspiring images. In addition, veterans can focus on inspiring images prior to sleep. These can be anything that promotes positive feelings. One veteran who had been tormented by nightmares for over thirty years used to hold his bamboo fishing rod, feeling its beauty and craftsmanship. He experienced almost immediate relief after his nightly focus. He would spend only about fifteen to twenty minutes, but it had a huge impact.

However, even more powerful are inspiring spiritual images, such as Christ, Buddha, Krishna, and Moses. Simply concentrating on those images prior to sleep tends to reduce the frequency of nightmares. But if veterans are not oriented to the spiritual life, then anything that promotes positive feelings can be effective.

Encouraging positive feelings towards others. A further step is to improve veterans' feelings in regard to others. Most veterans do not trust others, and have a general hostility to civilians. Helping them lower their hostility is a major coping skill that will greatly reduce nightmares.

If veterans are able to understand the relationship between their nightmares and their general hostility towards others, they may be motivated to reduce their hostilities.

The importance of respecting veterans' training. It is important to respect the military training that has instilled in veterans their current distrust and hostility. This training kept them alive on the battlefield in Vietnam and in the alleys and roads of Iraq. In addition, it is both impossible and clinically nonproductive to attempt to convince veterans that their feelings of distrust are no longer appropriate. They will simply dismiss you as not understanding the inherent dangers in our culture, and will categorize you as a civilian "who doesn't have a clue."

There are ways of working through veterans' general distrust of life by helping them appreciate that it is possible to stay alert while still looking for ways of liking others. This attempt to combine alertness and liking can be approached by discussing the "noble enemy concept." In earlier historical wars, the enemy was not dehumanized but rather was seen as an honorable foe who was worthy of battle. Most contemporary research indicates that veterans who hate the enemy and consider the enemy less than human have significantly more severe PTSD than do veterans who ascribe to the "honorable foe" concept.

This idea of the honorable enemy (and most Vietnam veterans had a respect for the NVA) helps veterans to accept the enemy's humanity.

The next step is to allow positive feelings to emerge towards others (i.e., civilians). It may be helpful to discuss with clients the logical perspective that how we choose to perceive our lives in our waking moments has an impact on how our dreams manifest during our sleep. That is, if veterans can continue to be alert and still be aware of their positive feelings for others, their dreams will be positively affected. However, this growth in awareness is slow and gradual.

Suicide/Homicide: "The Devil You Know...."

Frequently, veterans commit suicide because they believe that they are a "burden" on others and everyone will be "better off" if they are dead. Veterans may also believe that they were supposed to have died in the war, and that they "owe" it to the dead soldiers to follow them.

Substance abuse, of course, increases the probability of suicide. Suicide frequently occurs while veterans are using or drinking. Many times, the suicide is an accidental overdose taken because veterans are unable to stop the intrusive memories with their usual amount of drugs or alcohol.

It is impossible to stop those who are determined to kill themselves. However, it is possible to interfere with the process and possibly change that determination.

In Treatment, Discuss the Possibility of Suicide. We know that almost everyone who attempts suicide has talked about it and has informed individuals that they are "thinking" about it. In therapy, always openly discuss the possibility of suicide/homicide with veterans. Do they have a plan? Do they have the means to execute the plan? If they indicate that they intend to act on their plan, call 911. *Do not hesitate.* Veterans wish to be taken seriously, and this takes them seriously.

In addition they will take it as direct evidence that you truly care about them!

The Coexisting Possibility of Homicide. Coinciding with the suicide, frequently, is homicide. Veterans may kill someone close to themselves and then kill themselves. *If veterans indicate their intention to commit murder, therapists are required to call both the police and the intended victim.*

Veterans are a physically violent group. They have killed others in war, and many of them do not see the distinction between killing and murder. In addition, veterans may not take much responsibility for their behavior. Many of my clients who are veterans have asserted that once their anger passes a particular point, they are no longer responsible for their actions. Veterans need to be properly prepared to take responsibility for their actions as well as for their emotions.

These suicidal/homicidal tendencies actually may be increased by treatment due mostly to veterans being unprepared for the emotional impact of talking about their experiences. Therefore, it is important that any indication of suicide or homicide and the interaction with substance use/abuse be clearly dealt with in the sessions prior to beginning treatment (i.e., learning coping skills).

Reality Checks. Suicide contracts in which veterans agree not to commit suicide without first calling the therapist are relatively meaningless, but they nevertheless may provide some comfort to the therapist. More effective, however, is for therapists to have an honest exchange of emotions with the veterans who are their clients. It is important to let veterans know how we will be affected if they hurt themselves or others.

Secondly, if veterans have children, it is important to let them know how the suicide will interfere with their children's lives. Children's emotional development is seriously traumatized as a result of a parent's suicide, which also greatly increases the risk that children will choose suicide as an option in their adult life.

Thirdly, discuss what veterans expect will happen after the suicide. Frequently, veterans simply expect a cessation of their emotional pain; however, it is important to point out that the opposite may occur. That is, instead of the cessation of pain, their next existence may be even more painful, with no way of escaping. If veterans deny the possibility of an afterlife, remind them that no one knows, and that "it is better to deal with the devil you know than the devil you don't know."

PART III
UNDERSTANDING

"Don't let the winged dragon escape from the flask."
(Alchemical Warning)

Chapter One
Alchemy: The Royal Art
Working with the Nafs

The stilling of the heart is the true alchemy, which turns mercury into silver.[1]

Hazrat Inayat Khan

Alchemy, also known as the *ars regia* (the royal art), has as its basic process the *solve et coagule* (dissolution and reform) of the ego. If there is to be an emergence of the extraordinary, there has to be a breakdown of the ordinary.

Beliefs and Ego Development

Beliefs emerge as a result of ego development. The ego is constructed by the combination of several different levels of nafs. It is through our nafs that the world is filtered and our beliefs are developed. The increase of understanding by the nafs is the basis of ego development. In this system, the more advanced the ego development, the greater our understanding of existence.

Trauma is its own kind of alchemical process, which catalyzes ego development/fixation by causing the

---

1 Inayat Khan, *The Complete Sayings of Hazrat Inayat Khan* (New Lebanon: Omega Publications, 2010), 37.

nafs to become disorganized, resulting in a chaotic organization of existing beliefs. Prior to experiencing combat, a normal belief is that the world is relatively safe and predictable. While accidents in our regular world may occur, those experiences are rare and can usually be avoided. But in the war zone, when the first round goes by the head, a new realization occurs in which all previous beliefs are put into turmoil. The soldier is no longer certain regarding anything.

Treatment of combat PTSD is directed at reorganizing the nafs (i.e., improving ego development) into a dynamic system that integrates the traumatic information through the expansion of beliefs. When our existing beliefs are put into confusion we attempt to cope with the chaos in at least two ways. If our beliefs are inadequate to integrate the overwhelming experiences, we may change the information in order to maintain our beliefs, or we may change the beliefs to accommodate the new experiences. Changing the information is usually easier than changing beliefs. But changing beliefs is the way to Posttraumatic Growth.

Jim had been in the early invasion forces in Iraq. Insurgent forces attacked his convoy, and though they caused few American casualties, they sacrificed many of their own lives. Jim was shocked. "At first I thought that the *hajis* were just stupid. Then I began to realize that they didn't seem to care about their own lives. They had a cause and they were committed to it. I felt myself change as I saw that their fighting was not just a job but something more important than their lives.

I guess when I saw their dedication, I felt humble. But, of course, that didn't stop me from killing them."

For something pure (higher ideals) to emerge, the impure (ordinary beliefs) must break down. There must be a process of *de*struction in order to have *con*struction. Veterans are familiar with this in their boot camp/basic training phase, where they are first broken down—both physically and emotionally—and then rebuilt with the physical and mental training to kill.

Of course, not all veterans are the same. Everyone functions at different levels of ego development. The Sufis describe this in terms of different levels of nafs. As Pir Vilayat would say, "We need our ego. It is a sorry bull without his horns."

The understanding of an individual who experiences a traumatic incident tends not to increase. Such a person is fixated and suffering in ego isolation, and experiencing all the difficult emotional states that are tied to that isolation.

Nafs are similar to the Buddhist concept of the ego, as explained by Mark Epstein: "This view requires that the ego be understood as a complex and sophisticated matrix of structures, functions, and representations, rather than as a single entity that could be readily abandoned."[2]

---

2 See Epstein, Mark *Psychotherapy Without The Self: A Buddhist Perspective*, (New Haven: Yale University Press, 2007).

Chapter Two
Alchemical Stages of Ego Development
Nigredo/Separatio

Hazrat Inayat Khan discusses the stages of ego development as "degrees of intelligence." The Sufis describe the different complexes of nafs in terms of how the person perceives existence and is able to behave.

Nigredo/Separatio

In the alchemical process, the alchemist asserts that the experience of the *nigredo* (literally, the "blackness"—in this case, trauma which has plunged soldiers into a psychological state where nothing makes sense) produces the *separatio* (a scattering of the nafs), or the complete disruption of the individual's ego reality. This can be conceptualized as a breakdown in the relationship between elements of the self and the internalized representations of external reality. Many therapists contend that this stage is necessary in order for the unconscious to become conscious.

If the ego is able to function within the maelstrom of the separation, then ego development will be possible in terms of the realization of the more evolved nafs. Our ability to experience the confusion of ego change without undue resistance will eventually result in improved functioning.

Buddhists talk about the endurance of the ego as "going to pieces without falling apart."[3] The brilliant psychiatrist R. D. Laing was aware of this when he asserted that "All breakdown is not pathological; some breakdown is breakthrough."[4]

However, the dynamic process of ego change is not well supported in this culture. Most trauma therapists will focus on helping veterans regain their ordinary ego consciousness without taking advantage of the possibilities of ego development. Traumatized soldiers—due to lack of support of their new insights, overwhelming anxiety regarding being "different," lack of education regarding existence beyond the physical, and narrow and dogmatic religious doctrines—have little choice but to retreat to basic familiar, albeit crippling, ways of understanding.

The alchemists asserted that we must experience the nigredo—the darkness; or, in Jung's system, the facing/actualizing of our shadow—in order to transform the personality.[5] The shadow represents all the qualities we don't like in ourselves that we unconsciously project upon others.

Prejudice and discrimination are sometimes the result of shadow projection; so are violent attacks and wars. It would be difficult to justify attacks on other people if they did not represent our shadow.

3 See Epstein, Mark, *Going to Pieces Without Falling Apart* (New York: Harmony, 1998).
4 Laing, R.D., *Politics of Experience*, (New York: Pantheon Books, 1967).
5 See Jung, C.G. *Psychology and Alchemy* (Princeton: Princeton University Press,1968).

Our enemy in war usually represents our shadow, frequently, as manufactured by our government.

This may be why Christ said, "Resist not evil."[6] Perhaps he was urging us to meet our shadow and to care for it.

In the separation phase, however, there is the very real danger of decompensation. Decompensation is a process of ego breakdown (the nafs become scattered without the ego having an awareness of alternative dynamics) that results in the development of serious emotional difficulties (disruption of the lower nafs prior to accessing the more highly developed nafs) such as psychosis. For example, unless the ego is aware of the possibility of self-discovery, we may not have sufficient strength to endure the separatio of the nafs. In other words, the ego would fall apart, and the individual would experience serious confusion and despair—even hallucinations and flashbacks.

In alchemy it is said, "Do not let the winged dragon escape from the flask." This means that if we have a fragile container (an ego based on the lower nafs and unprepared for transformation), the dragon (our ability to function in the material world) will leave when the ego container is shattered. This results in psychotic states and living in a realm of unreality.

Ted had been living on the streets for over five years. When he served in Vietnam as a rifleman, he had experienced numerous firefights and seen many dead and wounded. Unfortunately, when he returned to stateside duty he became insubordinate, went AWOL, served time in the brig, and eventually received a dishonorable discharge. His dishonorable

6 Matthew 5:39.

discharge meant that he was ineligible for veteran's benefits through the Department of Veterans Affairs.

When Ted applied for treatment at the Vet Center where I was working, I requested an upgrade in his discharge, but it was denied by the Department of Defense. This meant that I could treat him, but I couldn't count him as a patient. All government agencies' budgets are determined by numbers of one kind or another. Not being able to count Ted meant that I would have to see more veterans eligible to be counted and see Ted essentially on my own time.

I agreed to see Ted in treatment. It soon became clear that he had become so traumatized by his Vietnam experiences that he was unable to interact with others except on a very basic level, where the threat of physical violence was always a distinct possibility. Ted no longer had the ability to understand others, to have an idea regarding others' motives other than to be able to assess threat. In fact, he was frequently in error regarding possible threats, and had become distrustful of almost everyone. This illustrated the alchemical process of trauma impacting a poorly developed adolescent ego, functioning at a basic level of nafs.

As we worked together, we gradually untangled his fears and distrust of psychotherapy. Yet it was clear that Ted was unable to adequately cope with the increased stress of any discussion of combat. Treatment without appropriate medication was not a possibility, and he refused to accept medication. Indeed, his fears and paranoia increased whenever the subject was broached. We settled into a slow process of maintaining safety and decreasing fears. Eventually, I was able to help him secure a small monthly sum from Social Security and find low-income housing. He manages and maintains.

Frequently, the lower nafs are able to withstand the onslaught of trauma. Then, instead of a breakdown/separatio, there is a hardening of veterans' beliefs, along with a disrupting of their usual internal processes. This results in increased anger and agitation, as veterans struggle with emotions that simply don't fit their existing beliefs.

Treating veterans who have been so damaged usually requires the help of medication and gradual work with reconstructing their ego. In such cases, it is important not to discuss alternative states of consciousness, as such discussions will increase their mental imbalance.

Phil was twenty-two and had been a tank driver in Iraq. During his tour, he plastered the inside of his tank with naked pictures of women, and would frequently masturbate to the pictures while driving the tank. Like many members of the armored cavalry, he regularly experienced the ability to inflict immense damage via his access to overwhelming firepower. Phil seemed to have relished the ability to destroy, and later, in treatment, he expressed great satisfaction in recounting how he had demolished houses.

Although resolute in his insistence that the Iraqis' resistance to the American forces was "ridiculous," Phil was agitated and angry. He found the nightmares, intrusive thoughts, and fear of loss of control confusing. "What is the matter with me?" he would plead. "Why am I feeling this way?"

Phil's dragon had not left his ego, yet it was awake, struggling with the boundaries of his self-concept. But even with this basic structure of nafs, known as "the demanding nafs," Phil had the opportunity for emotional growth and insight. If given the necessary treatment, veterans have the possibility of discovering a greater self, free from the boundaries of their previous, more narrow beliefs.

To survive the traumatic disruption of the ego requires a seemingly paradoxically strong ego. Someone with adequate ego strength (i.e., an awareness of an awakening) will be able to assimilate the traumatic experience without either being shattered or denying crucial aspects of the trauma. In other words, *the resilience of the ego is important if the trauma is to be both integrated into, and an active catalyst in transforming, the ego.*

Jim had been an F-4 pilot in Vietnam. During a strafing run, his aircraft was fatally damaged. He managed to eject and to land unharmed in a rice paddy near a village. However, the local villagers surrounded him almost immediately and began to beat him. Jim was convinced that if a jeep full of North Vietnamese soldiers hadn't arrived, the villagers would have killed him. The soldiers took him to a prisoner-of-war camp, where he spent the next seven years. Jim was tortured daily for the first three years.

Later, in treatment, he related to me, "I would tell myself that if it [the torture] didn't get any worse, that I could handle it. Then it would get worse, and I would tell myself the same thing until I eventually would pass out."

I administered several psychological assessments to Jim. Surprisingly, his profile suggested that he was a very high-functioning and psychologically healthy individual. I also had been very impressed by him in the face-to-face evaluations. Jim appeared to be a kind, considerate, intelligent, and friendly individual. He did not seem to have a trace of the symptoms of PTSD.

During our conversations, Jim said that he understood why the Vietnamese farmers had been angry: he had, after all, been strafing their village. He further understood his captors and their desperation to make him talk. He did not seem to harbor any anger or resentment towards his former enemy. "It was war, and they did what they had to do, as I was doing what I had to do." He had gone so far as to write a book about his experiences and become a motivational speaker.

Jim was someone who had managed to integrate his traumatic experiences by widening his beliefs. He truly experienced PTG.

A soldier's military training begins with the subordination of the individual self for the greater good of the military mission. However, military training specifies that self-sacrifice is to be focused on fellow soldiers. Civilians, with the exception of innocent women and children, are not deemed part of that group. In that sense, the training to minimize one's individual interests is narrow and restricted.

In addition, the training to be selfless is usually temporary, as is evident when the soldier is discharged. This is not to say that veterans will no longer protect the downtrodden and the disadvantaged. Many veterans devote their lives to service of the unfortunate and the defense of the weak. Those veterans have had a realization from their war experiences (PTG) that has shown them what is important in life. Other veterans, however, become encapsulated in their memories and fears. They isolate themselves, avoid social contact, and numb themselves with drugs and alcohol.

Our beliefs stand between reality and ourselves. My concept of God stands between God and myself. Trauma challenges our beliefs by forcing us to question and doubt our regular way of seeing the world. Trauma breaks us down, both emotionally and psychologically.

However, even if the ego is adequate to stand up under the traumatic experience, it is still problematic to expect the transformation. Transformation depends on many other factors besides just a healthy ego (i.e., a willingness to experience significant change in the self-concept).

The Demanding Self: Nafs al-ammara

Sufi descriptions are exquisite at describing the complexity of the ego. One of the most basic groups of nafs is termed, in Sufism, the "demanding self" (in Arabic, the *nafs al-ammara*). Pir Zia Inayat-Khan describes this level of ego development in this way:

The nafs al-ammara is the commanding self, the self that insistently demands every privilege and priority, and is unable or unwilling to recognize the existence of anyone but itself. It is perfectly natural and truthful for the One Being to pronounce "none exists but I," but when we, in the narrow confines of our mortal individuality, even tacitly imitate this sentiment, it is impudence. And yet this is what the nafs al-ammara does.[7]

Veterans with this level of ego development don't care about the result of their actions unless those actions produce difficulties for them. But when this group of nafs is separated from the other groups (i.e. from the other constructs of the ego), such as in the experience of trauma, the individual suffers from depression and anxiety. As Hazrat Inayat Khan guides us:

The training is to be wise in life, and to understand what we desire and why we desire it, and what effect will follow, what we can afford and what we cannot afford.[8]

The positive aspect of this nafs is that it develops self-confidence. Individuals with this type of developed ego are successful in ego-driven pursuits such as politics. This nafs asserts that "only I exist" and "only I matter." However, this type of perspective will also exacerbate the fear and avoidance that are part of the symptoms of PTSD.

Returning from war, veterans find themselves in a narrow and almost suffocating world. Veterans don't trust anyone who did not serve in the war zone, but they will also try to keep from discussing what they

---

7 Inayat-Khan, Zia
8 Inayat Khan, *The Gathas: The Training of the Ego. The Sufi Message* series, Volume XIII (Geneva: International Headquarters Sufi Movement, 1982), 175.

are experiencing with other veterans, due to a fear of being seen in a negative manner and/or bringing up memories they want to avoid, as well as with mental health practitioners. This sort of double bind is the result of several factors: the ego needing to maintain a sense of value (fearing that other veterans will consider the veteran "weak"); a hardening of the level of ego development (making the ego more resistant to development); and a response to military training (the "suck it up" factor), in addition to others.

However, this level of narrow ego development is confronted by the ego's desire to attain something greater than its current idea about itself: its self-concept. The resulting agitation of conflicting ego desire drives veterans to seek some sort of relief.

Concentration: "Whatever One Loves, One Gets"

In treatment, therapists can help veterans develop greater concentration. This calms the demanding self, at which point the next level of nafs begins to come into awareness. The Sufis view concentration as the process of holding a certain idea or object in the mind at all times. Hazrat Inayat Khan states, "The result of concentration depends on how much one loves the object of attainment. Whatever one loves, one gets."

Concentration I: A Practice to Reduce Agitation. Here is a good concentration exercise:

1. Ask veterans to choose something they care about. It could be a picture of a loved one, a flower, a picture of a saint, a landscape—anything they find inspiring and uplifting.

2. Then ask them to concentrate on the object for a few minutes, then close their eyes and visualize the object for a short period.

3. Have them repeat this practice several times a day.

This requires some self-discipline on the part of the veteran, and is best approached as a "training" to reduce their agitation. Veterans are oriented to think of tasks as "missions." With this concentration exercise, the mission is to reduce agitation.

Caring-about-Others Practice. The second part in reducing agitation and improving ego development is to help veterans experience that the more they care about others, even strangers, the less agitated they feel. Because the process of love is so important in the process of attainment, the process of attainment is more important than the object/person attained.

The Ego Ideal. Mark Epstein makes a similar point from a Buddhist perspective: "The concentration practices clearly promote unity of ego and *ego ideal* by encouraging fixity of mind in a single object.... The ego ideal is that towards which the ego strives, that which it yearns to become, that into which it desires to merge, fuse or unite." This is different from the *ideal ego*: "The ideal ego is an idea which the ego has of itself."[9]

Epstein's ego ideal seems similar to Hazrat Inayat Khan's *God-ideal*. The God-ideal is the manifestation of our greatest and most profound values. It is our embodiment of our highest ideals, and our recogni-

9 Epstein, Mark *Psychotherapy Without The Self: A Buddhist Perspective*, (New Haven: Yale University Press, 2007).

tion of those qualities in such great beings as messengers, saints, and prophets.[10]

Veterans who are struggling at the basic level of the demanding self will probably not be receptive to such a term as "God-ideal." It may be easier to talk about God in terms of what veterans may view as "more effective ways of living." Veterans may have dreams of achieving a college degree, aspirations to start a business, or simply ambitions to find regular employment. All individuals have aspirations. Veterans, like other people, want the future to be a particular way. The hopes expressed by veterans are the beginning of the formation of the greater self (the God-ideal).

Military training helps to change and transform the demanding self by emphasizing the subordination of the self in favor of the mission or the team. The individual needs are put aside, and the selfish nature of the nafs al-ammara is decreased in favor of hatred of the enemy and care for fellow soldiers. However, as is easily seen in the complaints and generally brutish behavior of the soldier, the ammara is alive and well—witness the well-documented rapes, killings, and general brutality of the soldiers to civilians in the war zones.

The nafs al-ammara considers others to be the cause of its limitation and therefore demands assertion of its own wishes irrespective of others. It understands freedom as freedom of the self, which it attempts to attain by self-gratification in any form.

Pir Vilayat Inayat Khan

---

10 See Inayat Khan, *Song of the Prophets: The Unity of Religious Ideals*, (New Lebanon: Omega Publications, 2009).

The nafs al-ammara is initially necessary in order to make our way in the world and not be taken advantage of. It is a survival mechanism. As one evolves, however, one sees that one's wellbing cannot be separated from the wellbeing of others, and so one reaches a second stage: the nafs al-lawwama.

Pir Zia Inayat-Khan

The Self-Accusing Ego: Nafs al-lawwama

The next stage of ego development is the self-accusing ego (in Arabic, *nafs al-lawwama*). The nafs al-lawwama is the critical self. These nafs are self-centered in terms of doubts, worries, and anxiety. This group of nafs depends on external authorities, such as science and religion, to give it confidence.

Pir Zia speaks of it as, "instead of just grasping and taking what it wants, it pauses to reflect and question itself and its motives." This critical self is in part an internalization of limitations experienced in life; the authoritarian parental voice that says "NO you cannot, you are incapable, you are unworthy."

In the military, this level of nafs is given voice through the superior officers. While soldiers have internalized their parents' voice (or lack thereof) to varying degrees, the officer's voice now takes precedent. Soldiers and Marines are trained to follow orders without thought, as their own lives and the lives of their fellow soldiers depend on their quickness to obey commands. Frequently, however, soldiers feel inadequate regarding their performance.

Jerry "walked point" for most of his tour in Vietnam—that is, he was the first soldier down a trail during a patrol. The point man's responsibility was to spot an ambush, booby traps, and anything suspicious that might get the men killed.

It was just getting dark, and his squad was making their way back through the jungle to their base. Jerry, an experienced point man, knew that it was too dangerous to go back the same way they had come. He picked a way through the jungle at random, and the squad followed. It was dense growth, and the men had to walk single file. The Viet Cong—whether because they were sufficiently mobile to adjust their ambush quickly to counter Jerry's choice, or because they were simply lucky—patiently let Jerry get through the ambush zone before they opened fire, killing the three soldiers caught in the middle of the patrol. The squad returned fire, and the VC quickly withdrew.

Although Jerry felt overwhelmed with guilt and failure, his training kicked in and he got his squad back to the base. However, there was no sanctuary there. His first lieutenant, seriously lacking in command skills, excoriated Jerry for "failing to be awake."

By the time Jerry finally came in for treatment with me, he had spent most of his post-military life drifting from one job to another, always trying to overcome that deep sense of failure and defeat.

He and I worked hard to uncover his sense of guilt and to develop the ability to accept himself. It became clear that self-accusation had turned his very admirable quality of caring so deeply about his duty and the other soldiers against him. Through the process of self-exposure, however, Jerry was able to expand his beliefs to include self-forgiveness. At one point, he suddenly realized that he had done the best he could and that he did not have to continue to torment himself.

This self-critical voice (or super-ego) can inhibit and have an immobilizing effect.

Self consciousness gives hardness to the expression of the lips, and it stiffens the tongue and makes the voice toneless, preventing a man from saying what he wishes to say....Its only remedy is forgetting self and putting the whole mind into work and each occupation undertaken.[11]

Hazrat Inayat Khan

This self-accusing level does include some positive qualities. One is that veterans begin to regret their selfish actions. They may still act in an angry and selfish manner, but afterwards they may wish they had not behaved so badly. *This is the beginning of the conscience.*

Jerry's conscience was alive and well, but overactive and punishing. However, now he had gained a greater awareness. How would he proceed?

One day, Jerry smiled and asked me, "You know, I feel pretty good. Am I cured?"

I replied, "When you think of the future, what do you want to have happen?"

Jerry looked surprised. He replied, "I don't know. I don't really think of the future. I have been so caught up in what happened, I never really think about what's going to happen."

I asked again, "What do you want to have happen?"

11 Inayat Khan, *Sacred Readings, The Gathas,* (Geneva: International Headquarters Sufi Movement, 1982).178.

He looked tired. Then he said, "I want to be happy. I want to have peace."

I asked him, "How will you make that happen?

Jerry looked thoughtful. "Maybe, with not having this bullshit I've been carrying around, I might be able to be happy."

Jerry had discovered that happiness came from within him, not from things he did. His sense of self expanded to include greater possibilities.

In Gestalt Therapy there is a saying that in order to move forward, we first have to know where we are standing. The nafs al-lawwama is the realization of where we are. Regret and repentance begin to be emotional processes that counteract the selfish nature of the nafs al-ammara.

...lawwamah is the condition of the mind which is full of thoughts, good and bad, over which the ego reigns, self covering the truth. He has bitterness or spite against another, or he has his ways of getting all he desires cleverly, or he finds faults with the others. He is worried about himself, anxious over his affairs, troubled about unimportant things, struggles along through life, being confused by life itself. It is not that his passions and emotions trouble him. What troubles him is his own thoughts and his feelings.[12]

Hazrat Inayat Khan

However, this nafs opens up the possibility for something larger. Although the struggle with feelings of guilt can produce regression into selfish acts and further fixate ego development, in their desire to

12 Inayat Khan, *The Complete Works of Pir-O-Murshid Hazrat Inayat Khan, 1923 II*, (London, The Hague: East-West Publications with the Nekbakht Foundation, 1989) 560.

mitigate these feelings of guilt, veterans may begin to look for something deeper in life.

Most likely, they will turn to exoteric religion available to everyone in an effort to find peace from their torments. Certainly, some relief can be found through two forms of the exoteric: fundamentalist and orthodox religions. If given absolute answers to their dilemmas, veterans may find at least temporary relief from their anxious states.

Accepting absolutist, dogmatic answers to existential dilemmas frequently relieves people of overwhelming anxiety. However, for many veterans, "John Wayne and Jesus Christ died in Vietnam"—meaning that they cannot reconcile the exoteric concept of God with the horrors they experienced. "If God is love," asks the veteran, "then why do we have such violent shit?"

The nafs al-lawwama considers itself to be the cause of limitation. It longs for freedom from the self and can therefore be of help in unlearning to identify with the limited self that one wishes to get rid of.

Pir Vilayat Inayat Khan

As combat veterans struggle with overwhelming experiences of depression, guilt, and anxiety, they also may retreat into extended substance abuse, reflecting the accusing self. Veterans frequently vacillate between religion and drugs/alcohol. Whatever substance or belief gives them momentary peace, it is held for a time.

Chapter Three
Coagule
The Building of the Self
Through Spiritual Practice

I f the alchemical process of solve (the breaking down of the self) has subsided and the self-accusing nafs have provided sufficient motivation for overcoming imagined self-limitations, the moment is there for the development of a greater awareness. This moment is the midwife of self-discovery, and provides the therapist's opportunity to aid in a monumental discovery for the veteran. The process of *coagule* (the rebuilding of the self) is aided through appropriate treatment that makes use of prayer and meditation. As the thought of a deity becomes more present, an ideal self develops.

A belief in something greater than our idea of our self (produced, by necessity, from the interaction between alchemy and the nafs) helps us surrender our self-image and allows a transformation of our sense of self. By forming an ideal self, the veterans may find not only relief from their torment but also states of consciousness that are beatific and ecstatic.[1]

---

1 See p. 153, for a meditation that specifically helps in the formation of the ideal self: the God-Ideal.

When our concept of our self is no longer useful—when it is obviously too limited—it is time for a new concept. Many individuals simply say they do not believe in God, but this is just another way of saying that they do not believe in their current concept of God. The opportunity now opens to form a new concept. As one counselor I know says, "If your God isn't working for you, then fire Him!"

But traumatized veterans are fixated by their combat experiences. Instead of acting as catalysts to free them from their narrow concepts of themselves, the traumatic experiences create mass confusion within the nafs. As more primitive levels of understanding in the development of the ego, the lower nafs are unable to assimilate the traumatic information into either the demanding self or the accusing self. To protect the ego, the nafs will increase their insular quality and withdraw from input. Many times, even other veterans are ignored if they do not agree with the traumatized veteran's ideas.

One way in which this phenomenon shows up is that veterans may become extremely patriotic, and reject any notions that the war was not a positive experience. This may even go so far as to deny that any atrocities may have been committed. Or they may act out in very violent ways, not caring whether they are injured or injure others. Veterans may develop a severe depression as they hold in their experiences. In such cases, they spend most of their time remembering their traumas but will not talk about them.

Because veterans spent much of their time in the war zone, escaping from either the boredom or the terror by being engaged in the fantasy of what would happen when they returned home, fantasy is familiar. Now, at home, fantasy becomes one way of avoiding the difficulties and pain of civilian life.

Because fantasy is a primary coping method, when veterans are under stress their fantasies increase. However, there is a reciprocal action: while the fantasies initially *decrease* stress, eventually they will *increase* the stress because they are being used to avoid reality.

If veterans retreat into fantasies when stress develops, they will not acquire the adequate coping skills to stay in the present; and as a result, stressor situations will become even more stressful.

Stress increases the tendency to generalize from one situation to another. The law of generalization states that "when anxiety increases, generalization increases." Stressful situations create anxiety, and that stress is generalized to similar situations. Thus, those new situations create anxiety and increase generalization to other similar situations—and so on, until veterans become isolated, withdrawn, and hostile.

If the state of anxiety continues, veterans become uncommunicative and resist attempts at intimacy. If veterans are fixated in the demanding self, they may become abusive to their spouse and children, abuse alcohol, and develop extreme notions of entitlement. Veterans will resent civilians, anyone who opposed the war (including other veterans), and most politicians.

If veterans are fixated in the accusing self, they will be consumed by guilt. They will experience intense suffering from their previous actions during the war, which may not necessarily include atrocities or even anything but the most understandable of actions.

They will feel haunted by their actions in a fire-fight, where the enemy was trying to kill them and everyone was well-armed and well-trained. Taking another life changes anyone. Killing is a universally acknowledged initiation into being another type of person. This is especially true of veterans, who took into themselves the military training to dehumanize the enemy.

Believing the enemy to be less than human makes the killing easier *during* the war. However, this also makes life more difficult *after* the war. After the war, the enemy may be granted his humanity by our country, requiring veterans to change their view of their enemy. It is one thing for the country to assert that the enemy now has human status; it is quite an-other thing for veterans, who have been steeped in the indoctrination of dehumanization, to shift their emotional investment to an acceptance of the former enemy.

Anger is a major symptom of this fixation, and it helps to maintain the insular quality of the nafs. A function of these lower, or earlier, nafs is to preserve their limited understanding. They attempt to main-tain their views by justifying their emotions and needs. A conscience that is poorly developed will not create guilt but instead, a mild paranoia and a mistrust of authority.

If veterans are in the accusing self and have devel-oped a conscience, the primary symptoms are guilt and anxiety.

Some veterans have discovered that much of their guilt is relieved if they work with their former enemy. Many have returned to their former places of combat and involved themselves in projects such as helping to build hospitals. Others have returned and gone on bike tours, discovering a new image of those against whom they fought, and returning with positive memories that help offset their intrusive negative images.

But most veterans, at this stage, struggle daily with a severe depression, panic attacks, deep guilt, and desperate cries in the night. Their guilt is two-fold: they despair of both their actions and their very survival. They express great amazement that they survived, and equal regret when so many others did not. Not understanding why some survived and others didn't increases their confusion, causing them to reject the simplistic solutions offered by fundamentalist religion.

Some veterans, in their despair, have forced an open expansion of their belief in God, saying, "God didn't have anything to do with it. We have free will. We chose it. But God forgives us."

Others, caught in deeper throes of guilt, are unable to attend spiritual ceremonies. They can't bear to bring themselves before God. They believe that their sin was so great that they cannot be forgiven.

And yet there are many veterans who do not believe that they have any guilt. They believe that they did the "right thing" then, and that they would do it again. They grieve for their dead comrades and may wonder why they were spared, but they deny any suggestion that the war (any war) was a mistake and that there were atrocities. These veterans insist, "War is what it is. It has been here since time began and it will always be here. Yes, there are civilians who are hurt, but that can't be helped. Our soldiers are the finest fighting force in the world. The enemy may also be well-trained and able fighters, but they cannot match our bravery and dedication to a higher ideal."

These individuals do not appear to be bothered by their conscience. Their sense of what is right is centered on nationalism. They come into treatment because they loved war. They loved the adrenaline, the heroism, the meaningfulness of that life. Now, as civilians, they feel out of place. How do they fit in with this very boring existence? The alchemy of combat opened them to an energy that won't let them sleep. They awaken at 2:00 in the morning and have to get up while the rest of the world is asleep. They prowl through their house, check their perimeter, try to distract themselves, and wish they had a purpose.

They want further understanding of reality, a deeper and more profound awareness; and society does not offer any obvious sense of relief. These veterans enter treatment and may be met with medication and therapy that helps them to "readjust," meaning accept the status quo.

Helping Veterans Develop an Ideal Self

In treatment, ask those veterans to think of someone they admire. It is better if they don't actually know the person. Then ask them what was it about that person that was inspiring? Most veterans have no problems with this part. Then ask them to recognize that the qualities they admired in that other person are also in themselves.

Fred had been a dismount, an infantry soldier on a Bradley fighting machine in Iraq. Now he was struggling with "What am I going to do with my life? I could just go back and be a waiter, I could go to school, I could do a lot of things. But nothing seems very interesting."

I asked him, "Is there anyone you can think of, throughout history, whom you have admired? Someone you don't know."

Fred thought for a minute and then said, "Bill Gates. The way he did things. He just did it, he knew what he wanted."

"So you liked the way Gates was focused and goal directed."

Fred looked skeptical. "No," he corrected me, "I liked the fact that he was ruthless; that guy didn't let anyone get in his way. When I was in Iraq, I realized that to get what I wanted I had to be ruthless." He paused. "Maybe you're right—another way of saying "ruthless" is to say he was focused. I guess it's more acceptable to be focused than it is to be ruthless. But I don't give a shit! I just want to know what I want, and then I'll know what to do."

"What do you think Gates wanted?"

Fred smiled. "I used to think that it was just power. But now I think there was more to it. I think that he had a vision. Power was just what happened when he took risks and won." Fred's enthusiasm was obvious.

"What is your vision?" I asked.

He grimaced. "I have an idea, but I don't know. Maybe it will work and maybe it won't."

"It sounds like you admire Gates both for his vision and his ability to get things done."

"Yeah, sure."

"*You* have those qualities of ideas and making ideas an actuality in you. You wouldn't have seen them in Gates if you didn't also have them in yourself. You wouldn't have recognized them."

He frowned. "You're saying I could be Bill Gates?"

"No, I'm saying that what you admire about Gates is in you. Gates is just showing you how you could be."

This is part of the construction of the ideal self. In the construction of the ideal self, we bring to our consciousness our greatest and most profound beliefs. Of course, our self-concept is different from our concept of our ideal self. However, it is important to begin to imagine that our ideal is part of who we are. Regardless of how little we believe that we currently manifest the qualities of our ideal, we must begin with the possibility that those qualities are within us—dormant, possibly, but still within us.

For veterans, just the thought that there is a spark of surprise may be enough of a catalyst to move them from despair to hope. Unfortunately, despair is frequently deeply entrenched. Many times, veterans were faced with no-win situations. If they didn't kill the child carrying the grenade or the woman with the rifle, then their fellow soldiers would die.

A Korean War Navy veteran had been stationed on a destroyer during most of his tour of duty. They were patrolling just off the coast of Korea and had been instructed to intercept a battalion of the North Korean Army as it moved south.

They soon spotted the battalion of North Korean troops moving south along the mountainous coast. The troops were trapped against the mountain's cliffs on one side and the ocean on the other. There was no escape from the ship's guns. The mountain's cliffs were too steep to climb, and the ocean was rocky and treacherous.

The ship prepared to start shelling the North Korean troops; but the spotter had seen through his binoculars that the North Koreans had anticipated this situation and had forced hundreds of innocent villagers to march with them.

Over the destroyer loudspeakers, it was announced to the villagers in Korean that shelling was to begin. The spotter reported that many of the villagers attempted to run away, but were shot by the North Koreans.

There was a pause while the command contemplated the horror that was about to ensue. Soon, the ship began to shell both the troops and the villagers. The veteran who later came into treatment with me was responsible for aiming a battery of guns. He could see the explosions as the shells landed among the troops and the villagers.

There was a great screaming mixed with the explosions, and the men on board the destroyer could see bodies and parts of bodies flying through the air. Finally, the shelling stopped and the ship moved on.

For the past fifty years, ghosts have awakened the Navy veteran from his sleep. They stand there silently in his room, pointing their outstretched arms at him accusingly. Sometimes he gets up and swings at them, but they disappear and he is left standing while his wife stirs and awakens. She comforts him and he returns to bed. Other times, he just lies there and looks at the ghosts while he cries.

This veteran was very religious, but felt inadequate to pray or have any conscious contact with God. After a long process of ego construction in treatment, he finally was able to perform ritual cleansings according to his religion. It took several repetitions of the ritual, but eventually the ghosts disappeared.

I told this story to a spiritual teacher of mine. He paused and then said, "It's war." Very true: the detritus of war continues long after the battlefields are silent.

For this veteran, there were few choices during the war. He could have refused the order and ended up in the brig. The skipper could have not fired the guns and then been responsible for the deaths of many American soldiers as the North Koreans invaded South Korea.

Chapter Four
Sublimatio and Circulatio

The alchemical solve can result in what is termed the *sublimatio*. The sublimatio is the rising above the chaos of the solve. The sublimatio is a direct experience of the ideal self. Afterwards, however, there is a return to the solve and then another sublimatio. Veterans frequently recount the experience of transcendence in battle. The sudden awareness of higher states of consciousness and then the dropping back into the terror state. This process of rising above and then returning is termed the *circulatio*. The circulatio is psychologically experienced as the development of insights in the expansion of the self-concept that allow the integration of the traumatic experience into the expanded belief systems, also known as "accommodation".

Without the formation of the ideal self, however, the veteran will instead experience the circulatio as dissociation and alienation. As a result of his narrow self-concept, he will resist the memories of the traumatic experiences and become more isolated, depressed, and anxious.

The formation of the ideal self helps to decrease the dissociative danger of the circulatio and to contain the

137

opposing forces unleashed by the traumatic catalyst. The rising above and returning, if supported in treatment by a therapist who has experienced transcendent states, has the potential to create insights that develop the expanded sense of self. This expanded sense may allow the integration of the traumatic information.

The ideal self includes the experience of acting out of innate awareness—a soul awareness—rather than the ordinary self formed from interaction with the world. The soul motive is generally referred to as "altruism," or simply as the act of service without needing a material reward. The soul motive can also come about through the recognition of immanence—that God is present now!

Acting from soul motives is well-known in society as a way out of apparently insoluble conditions. In the movie *Gandhi*, the Mahatma is confronted with a Hindu who confesses: "I am going to hell. I murdered two Muslim children after the Muslims murdered my family." Gandhi replies, "You may indeed go to hell. But there may be a way out. Find two orphaned Hindu children and raise them as Muslims." Trauma—by displacing our central values of self-identity, by forcing the confrontation with our basic assumptions regarding our interactions with the physical world, and refusing to be ignored—opens up awareness to vastly greater potentialities within physical life.

The process of expanding beliefs in order to integrate traumatic information is greatly facilitated when veterans realize that the qualities they so admire in others are actually in themselves. In this way, the ideal self becomes actualized in new beliefs.

When we recognize greatness in someone else, we are able to recognize that same greatness in ourselves. That greatness is evident in how we behave, how we treat others, and how we care for others.

This gave the next lesson, that the kingship is not in the outer wealth but in spirituality, that even the king stands humbly at the door of the God-realized man.[1]

Hazrat Inayat Khan

A famous Sufi story often told by Pir Vilayat illustrates this point.

A great spiritual teacher lived in a small village in India. He dressed in rags, but was in reality a great holy man.

Because the man was a great spiritual teacher, the king of India decided to visit him. When the village heard of the king's impending visit they became quite excited and began lavish preparations for the royal visit.

On the day of the king's visit the old man went to sit beside the road. He sat with his legs outstretched and the bottoms of his feet facing the road. In India, and in most Middle Eastern countries, it is a sign of serious disrespect to show the bottoms of your feet.

The first people along the road were policemen, unaware of the reason for the king's visit, and had been sent to secure the road for the king. One of the policemen saw the old man with his feet out and went over to the old man. "Hey, pull in your feet!" the policeman said very roughly. The old man looked at him and said, "That is why."

---

1 Inayat Khan, *Religious Gatheka* #56.

The policeman was quite intimidated and decided to let his lieutenant take care of the matter. The lieutenant, upon seeing the old man, swore under his breath at the policeman, and went over to the old man. "Sir," the lieutenant began, "you must pull in your feet as the king is coming." The old man looked at the earnest face of the Lieutenant and said, "That is why."

The lieutenant was quite flummoxed and decided that he would leave it to his rival the captain of the guards. Soon the captain came along. He was a dignified man with a quiet authority. He came over to the old man and said respectfully, "Sir, you know the king is coming, do you have a reason for sitting here with your feet out like that?" The old man looked at the quiet in the captain and said, "That is why." The captain paused and thought he would be very interested in how the king's secretary might handle this old man.

Soon the secretary came along the road. He paused in front of the old man, put his hands together in the prayer position, bowed deeply, and said, "Most honorable sir. It would be a great favor to me if you would please pull in your feet as the king is coming." The old man bowed in return to the God within the secretary and said, "That is why." The secretary became lost in ecstasy at this point and realized that the king must meet this old man.

The king came. He was riding on an elephant surrounded by guards, courtiers, and soldiers. When he saw the old man he ordered the procession to halt. The elephant knelt and the king descended from his chair. He walked over to the old man and prostrated himself. The king gradually arose to his knees in the prayer position, and remained silent for some time. Finally the king spoke, "Most venerable one, how long have you been sitting there like that?" The old man smiled and said, "Ever since I stopped holding out my hand, and that is why."

That is why the policeman was a policeman, the lieutenant a lieutenant, and so on. It was all in how they treated the old man. How we treat others is reflective of our evolution and our level of realization that allows us to access the different nafs. The old man had realized something far beyond our ordinary states and was no longer dependent on this world.

The alchemical action of repeated traumas of combat upon various stages of ego development destroys and creates beliefs, and, depending on the level of ego development, stimulates despair, grief, anger, fear, anxiety, nightmares, and other aspects of PTSD. Through the construction of an ideal self, the alchemical dynamic may also stimulate Posttraumatic Growth (PTG).

Chapter Five
Beliefs

All beliefs are simply degrees of clearness of vision.[1]

Hazrat Inayat Khan

Our goal, as therapists, is to help veterans expand their belief systems, through the construction of an ideal self, to integrate the traumatic information of combat and discover new inspiration. Combat changed how veterans perceive the world. As a result of combat, veterans have new information regarding life's possibilities and actualities. However, their belief systems aren't able to integrate the information. The new knowledge is too big; it won't fit into their existing ways of understanding.

Ted had been a Marine in Vietnam. For six sessions in treatment, we processed his childhood, adolescence, and military training. He told me that when he went to Vietnam in 1968, landing in Da Nang, at first he didn't have any weapons. Then he was eventually given an M16, web gear, Kaybar knife, canteens, and ammunition. He was reportedly in a "daze." He was still enthralled with being in a tropical country filled

---

1 Inayat Khan, *The Inner Life* (Geneva: International Headquarters of the Sufi Movement, 1979), 45.

with jungle, and only faintly aware that there was an enemy.

"I remember when the war got personal. I had been in Vietnam just a couple of days when I heard a sniper round go past my head. I couldn't believe that someone I didn't even know was trying to kill me. I wanted to find him and tell him that I was a good guy. I wanted him to know there was no reason to try and kill me."

"The war became real."

"Yeah! Everything changed."

Ted had a difficult time understanding that complete strangers were trying to kill him. His training had not prepared him mentally for this obvious fact of war.

In another instance of treatment, Archie, an Army soldier, had recently returned from Iraq, where he had been a dismount on a Bradley fighting machine. A Bradley is an awesome machine of destruction.

It had been difficult for me to establish a therapeutic rapport with this veteran. However, after Archie was able to process his earlier periods of military training, he began to focus on his more recent combat experiences.

"You couldn't trust any of the *hajis*," he told me. "They don't have the same way of believing in life the way we do. They would use women and children to throw grenades, and come at us with AKs."

"It's difficult for me to understand how horrible it must have been to have to kill women and children," I told him.

"It was the worst part. I can't forgive myself for what I had to do. I mean, I see people now who say to me, "Great job!" They don't know what I did. If they knew, they wouldn't be buying me beers and dinner."

Archie's ideas about being fair, fighting an honorable enemy, and maintaining dignity had been shattered. He hated the insurgents. They had violated basic human rights in how they fought.

Formation of Beliefs

Unless we grew up in a very chaotic environment, we believe that life changes in gradual ways. We age, we gain knowledge, we increase our understanding—and we do all that gradually. Yes, there are tragedies of sudden death; but those things happen to other people. We form assumptions that our life changes will proceed in an orderly and gradual manner.

Most of us develop a fear of sudden change. We find comfort in predictable, routine living patterns. Winning the lottery is often cited as a stressful experience that changes the winner's life into a nightmare of paranoia and depression.

Even in driving our cars, we experience the myth of invulnerability—our belief that we will not be harmed as long as we maintain attention, drive defensively, and obey the rules of the road. Auto accidents that occur in spite of careful driving are overwhelming, traumatic experiences. We thought we had control over our lives—and suddenly, in a moment, our control is revealed to be an illusion.

Assimilation and Accommodation

Jean Piaget, the great French psychologist, asserted that there are two primary ways we organize new information to form new beliefs—assimilation and accommodation.[2]

---

2 See Piaget, Jean. *The Essential Piaget*, ed. Gruber and Vondeche

Assimilation occurs when our belief systems are adequate to incorporate the additional knowledge. We simply add the information to the existing beliefs. It is like discovering that our friend likes Chinese food as well as American food. This information does not challenge our concept of our friend.

However, assimilation is not possible if belief systems can't manage the new information. The suddenness of death in a combat assault is shocking. Soldiers are unable to grasp the reality of the sudden loss of a comrade. "He just wasn't there any more. His body was there but he wasn't in it. It was fucking awful. Death. I mean, what the fuck? But now I know I was just stupid. That's just what happened. It got so it didn't mean nothing. It couldn't."

The second method of organization, *accommodation*, works in one of two ways. One is that when the new information does not require too great a change in our beliefs, we simply change the beliefs.

"You know," one veteran told me, "I trusted officers. I thought they were better-trained and smarter. That was bullshit. It only took one time for the lieutenant to give me a stupid order to know that he was a true dumb ass."

But when we are not able to change the beliefs, then we change the information. As one veteran put it, "All that crap about how we tortured people in Iraq. I was at that prison. All I saw were terrorists who were damn lucky to have a place to sleep and something to eat."

Changing beliefs is a difficult task. Most of our beliefs are based on our life experiences. Our beliefs

(New York: Basic Books, 1977).

145

determine how we think, how we perceive the world, our expectations, and how we relate to others.

In the belief of every person there is some good for him; and to break that belief is like breaking his God.[3]
Hazrat Inayat Khan

Because our beliefs are based on our experiences, we look outside of ourselves to confirm our beliefs. It is the rare individual whose inner life is sufficiently developed to form beliefs based on inner awareness.

Mullah Nasreddin was searching outside his house. A friend stopped by and asked him what he was looking for. Nasreddin answered that he had dropped the key to his house. The friend began to help him and the two men crawled around on the ground looking under every rock and twig. Finally the friend asked the mullah, "Where did you drop the key?" Nasreddin answered, "Inside the house." The friend looked incredulous and angrily asked, "Then why are searching out here?" The mullah calmly answered, "There is more light out here."

We have a circular process of forming and establishing beliefs. Once our beliefs are established in childhood, they direct how we choose to think, perceive, and act. New beliefs are formed as a result of the consequences of our actions.

But our ordinary reality, filtered through our beliefs, may feel flat and empty. There is something in us that rebels against the boredom of our materialistic lives. Something tells us there is more to life than material gain and entertaining technology.

---

3 Inayat Khan, *The Complete Sayings of Hazrat Inayat Khan* (New Lebanon: Omega Publications, 2010), 23.

Combat veterans, whether from the jungles and rice paddies of Vietnam, or the alleys and roads of Iraq, either rejected or ignored by society, may have tried to forget their experiences by investing themselves in work, alcohol, fighting, and drugs. Sometimes, something of the horror and torment subsides; but there is always the residue, the detritus of the killing and the blood that challenges their ordinary beliefs.

Tim had been back from Iraq for about a year before his family insisted that he seek help. He had not worked since his discharge. He had been a tank driver in the Army. He was twenty-two.

"I know that nobody understands. Everyone thinks that I should forget what happened and go to work. Make money. Get married. Have a family. Be happy."

"What's it like to be told that?"

"Oh, it's OK. I try to get along."

"How do you respond when people say that?"

"How *do* I respond or how do I *want* to respond?"

"Tell me."

"I want to tell them to fuck off. But I know that they still think that my making money can make them happy. So I tell them that they're right. I don't even know how to tell them what is with me. I don't know why I feel this way. Doc, am I crazy?"

"You went through something that civilians never experience. You understand the world in a way none of us will ever understand. You have an advantage on us. You know what can happen in an instant."

If veterans want to reinstate civilian beliefs, they have to give up the beliefs that kept them alive in the war zone. Civilian belief systems can't coexist with the reality of veterans' beliefs. Civilians ignore inherent dangers of being in a crowd, the possibility that snipers have us in their sights, and that going to and from work the same way each day allows for the possibility of booby traps/improvised explosive devices (IEDs) and ambushes.

PTSD is at least partially the result of the failure of our culture to provide the opportunity of an adequate civilian belief system for veterans. An adequate belief system would include how to integrate the reality of combat with civilian life. The idea of patriotism is supposed to suffice for the rationale of war. There are few combat veterans who do not quickly realize that wars are not about patriotism, but instead, are about staying alive and helping one's comrades to survive. Political rationales are meaningless in combat.

People whose belief systems are not adequate to incorporate combat experiences may change the information to fit their already constructed beliefs. In this case, they will alter their understanding of the event in order to fit their beliefs. Thus, they change the information that they have killed civilians into dissociation, a removing of their self-concept from the situation.

Ralph was a Vietnam veteran who had been in the infantry: a "grunt." He had been in innumerable firefights and search-and-destroy patrols.

Ralph came into treatment agitated. "You know, it doesn't seem real. When I think about it, I remember all this stuff; but I know I'm just making it up. It couldn't have happened that way."

"What about your memories don't seem real?"

"We didn't do those things. We fought and we killed people but we had to. They were trying to kill us."

"What sort of things didn't you do?"

There was a long pause. He looked at the floor. He looked at the clock. Then he spoke: "OK! But it wasn't me. I was different. I had to be that way. I was just trying to stay alive." He began to sob.

"Can you care about that young man who was just trying to survive? Can you tell him that he is OK?"

Sobbing, he cried, "Fuck, I don't want to know him. He is a scary guy."

The process of accommodation occurs constantly in combat. Because it is difficult to change the information regarding the experiences of dead and wounded, so dissociation (denial of involvement) occurs. Yet as much as veterans deny and dissociate from the violence of combat, memories eventually become intrusive and force their way into consciousness. Those intrusive memories create depression and anxiety as veterans continue to attempt to avoid their feelings of grief.

Those beliefs that allow civilians to work and function within society are not adequate for veterans. Veterans have seen and participated in the violent, bloody acts of war. Civilians' belief in a safe, predictable world is no longer viable for them.

The veterans have something to tell their nation about how to deal with other problems that are likely to happen, problems that will not look different from Vietnam. Out of our sufferings, we should learn something.[4]

Thich Nhat Hanh

Soldiers, upon entering the war zone, operate in a different level of awareness. Their training has instilled

4 Thich Nhat Hanh, *Peace Is Every Step* (New York: Bantam Books, 1991).

a new set of assumptions/beliefs: that their environment is hostile, dangerous, and life-threatening. They attempt to be fully alert to their entire surroundings. Their lives and the lives of others depend on their actions.

If soldiers survive combat, the lessons learned there are never forgotten. New beliefs are formed in battle and are carried into civilian life. Veterans consider the new beliefs to be more valid than their previous civilian beliefs. Regardless of how maladaptive those beliefs are in civilian life, veterans are extremely unlikely to discard them.

Tom started having panic attacks about two months after his return from Iraq. He had served in the Army as part of a quick reaction force (QRF). The QRF responded to sudden calls for help from patrols under heavy enemy fire. The entire force had to always be ready for a response, and frequently encountered stiff resistance from the enemy.

"People don't understand how quickly things happen. I could never just let down even on my off time. I never knew if another QRF was going to need us. Now I can't be in crowds. I can't control the situation."

"What happens?"

"Shit, my heart starts racing and I start sweating. At first I thought I was having a heart attack, but the doctor told me it was just a panic attack. *Just!* I wonder if she ever has panic attacks."

"If other people were more aware of the possibilities," I asked him, "do you think you would be better able to function?"

"Of course. If other people were as aware as I am, I wouldn't have to take on all this pressure. I would feel more like I could count on them. But that's not going to happen. They're too stupid and lazy. God!" he concluded, "I would really like to go back to Iraq."

Tom's beliefs in the likelihood of sudden violence made him an effective and superior soldier in the dangerous war zone. But in his civilian work, his level of combat readiness was interfering.

Lessons learned in combat are not so important in civilian life. Many times, the lessons learned become known as symptoms of PTSD. For example, the need to be always alert if continued into civilian life is termed "hypervigilance" in PTSD symptoms.

Many soldiers have a sense of invulnerability during combat, similar to civilians' sense when driving. I have had soldiers tell me that they believed they were immortal for most of their tour of duty. It was only when someone close to them was killed that they realized their own mortality. Usually their friend had followed all the right orders, had done what was necessary to survive, and may even have helped other soldiers learn how to exist in a war zone. Then suddenly, in the chaos of a moment, the friend was gone forever.

Instead of changing belief systems to accommodate the traumatic experience, soldiers may use a variety of coping methods to maintain their belief systems and their ability to continue fighting. The most common temporary coping method is to drink alcohol or use drugs.

Another coping strategy is to try and reduce the overwhelming grief by negating the importance of their loss. Soldiers attempt to minimize their traumatic experiences with phrases such as, "It don't mean shit," or "Drive on." While in the war zone, alcohol, drugs and avoidance of memories allows the regular inadequate belief systems to remain intact; but those strategies are less effective in civilian life when another intrusive thought occurs or a sweaty nightmare interrupts sleep.

In order to effectively participate in civilian society, veterans have to accommodate the beliefs that were formed in battle. These coping methods of avoidance are temporary, and ultimately increase the severity of PTSD. Trauma-shattered beliefs provide minimal support, as veterans struggle to hold onto the remnants of their sense of the world. Treatment is not helpful if it simply confronts veterans' chaotic ideas without providing realistic alternatives, such as either noting the advantages veterans may have in emergency situations or emphasizing veterans' greater knowledge of the violent possibilities in life.

I have presented many theoretical and applied papers on treatment of PTSD at international conferences. During my attendance at the conferences I also listened to the presentations of other therapists. I found many stimulating and informative perspectives and experiences. But there were also presentations that made me shudder as I contemplated veterans facing such a difficult treatment approach. In one such presentation, the therapists were proposing that veterans think of themselves as being from another planet, and so the life skills the veterans learned on that other planet would not work on this planet. In order to live on this planet, they suggested, veterans would have to stop behaving as if they still lived on their home planet.

As trauma therapists, we are all well-intentioned and working hard to help veterans. But to confront veterans, who are already feeling estranged from society, with further evidence that they don't belong; to ask them to discard those very behaviors that have kept them alive; and to ignore the validity of their beliefs formed on the battlefield, is not helpful.

Helping veterans change beliefs, however, is a slow and gradual process. If too much is presented too soon, increased resistance occurs, beliefs become more fixed in their structure, and veterans may withdraw from treatment.

The Perfect Friend

It is crucial to have a trusted spiritual friend who suspends any of the kind of judgments the nafs al-lawwama is apt to make with regard to oneself, and reminds one of who one really is.

Pir Vilayat Inayat Khan

An exercise that helps veterans continue the process of developing an ideal self through the formation of new beliefs takes place in a guided meditation. The meditation called "The Perfect Friend" helps with concentration, widening perspectives, and changing beliefs.

While the exercise is better done with the eyes closed, it can also be done with the eyes open; some veterans may find it too uncomfortable to close their eyes during this exercise.

Ask veterans to imagine that they have a friend they can trust. They can tell this person anything, and their friend will never betray them. Now, have veterans think of more qualities for this friend. Give them some time to think; but be aware that veterans are not used to this sort of concentration and their minds will quickly wander.

As a way of helping them stay with the exercise, you may want to suggest some qualities, such as:

＊ **Loyalty**: this friend will always be there for you, this friend will always be honest, this friend will not tolerate your anger but also will never be afraid of it;

＊ **Strength**: this friend has an unlimited amount of strength, both emotional and empathic;

＊ **Light**: this friend seems to have an inspiring quality that lifts your spirits;

＊ **Understanding**: it is clear that this friend understands you, this friend grasps the meaning behind what is being said. It isn't necessary to constantly explain yourself. The friend understands; and

＊ **Compassion**: this friend cares about you, but not in a way that ignores your shortcomings. This friend knows how you could be, not how you should be.

After veterans have finished the exercise, ask them to accept the friend as themselves. Point out that they could not have known about those qualities if they did not have those same qualities in themselves. The perfect friend is the veteran's own self.

This exercise challenges self-concepts and ordinary beliefs, and can be the first step in accommodation/ expansion of beliefs.

Belief is the means and not the end. Belief leads to realization; it is not that we come to a belief. If a man's foot is nailed on the ladder, that is not the object.... Those therefore who believe in a certain creed, in a

religion, in God, in the hereafter, in the soul, in a
certain dogma, are no doubt blessed by their belief and
think they have something, but if they remain there,
there is no progress.[5]

Hazrat Inayat Khan

Enabling Fluid Beliefs

A fluidity of beliefs is important for both therapists
and veterans. For accommodation of beliefs to occur,
it is important for therapists and veterans to be willing
to work out of a flexible reality.

Joe had served in the Army in Vietnam as an infantryman, a grunt. He had been through innumerable
firefights, had seen many wounded and dead, and had
never talked about it. After returning home, Joe had
become an anti-war protester and had decided that
the war had been "meaningless." He now believed
that everyone who had died had died for "nothing."

Joe was having a particularly difficult time at work
because of his very strict "by-the-book" attitude. He
made life unpleasant for his fellow workers, but was
resolute in his beliefs.

"Isn't this the job?" he complained to me in treatment.
"Aren't we supposed to be paying attention to the details? I mean, what is the matter with everybody?"

"It sounds like you can't trust the other workers."

"No, it's not that I can't trust them. It's just that I
don't believe that they pay attention."

---

5 Inayat Khan, *Complete Works of Pir-O-Murshid Hazrat Inayat*
Khan: Original Texts: Lectures On Sufism: 1924 II: June 10-End of
December (New Lebanon: Omega Publications with the Nekbkaht
Foundation, 2009).

"What do you experience when you are with the other workers?"

"Man, I just want to get away from them. They may get themselves hurt, and I don't want to be responsible."

"This was true in Vietnam. If you didn't pay attention, people died."

"Yes. But these people don't understand that. It's like they live in some fantasy land where people don't get hurt."

"What happens when you try to communicate what you know?"

"It's a waste of time. They ignore me or they just shrug and keep on doing it the same way."

"They don't have the benefit of your Vietnam experience?"

"Well, yeah I guess," he laughed. "I guess maybe Vietnam was good for something."

"Are there any other advantages you have as a result of being in Vietnam?"

"Maybe. I never thought of it like that. I always just thought of it as a waste of lives."

"What is it like to think of Vietnam differently?"

"I don't know. This is new. I'm going to have to give it some thought."

"It's hard to change ways of thinking about such an emotional issue," I said.

Joe had become very secure in his way of thinking about Vietnam. He was comfortable in his despair, his anger, and his justified railings against the politicians, the officers, and the Pentagon for their misman-agement, ineptness, and insensitivity. He was fearful that if he began to see positive aspects of his experience, he would be allowing the "war criminals" to get away with their crimes.

The Process of Changing Beliefs.

The process of changing beliefs works best if it proceeds slowly and carefully. It is important to realize that changing one belief ("there may have been something positive that came out of Vietnam") does not mean that other related beliefs (the incompetence of officers, the killing of civilians, and the loss of American lives) are also negated. Most important is to discover the belief that stands in the way of progressing.

The practice of a spiritual path that challenges automatic thoughts and authoritarian/dogmatic statements also helps to challenge ineffective belief systems. If the concept of God is understood to be a concept—limited as all concepts are; and, being limited, not adequate to actually contain God—then the spiritual path is helpful.

I am He whom I love, and He whom I love is I,
We are two spirits dwelling in one body.
If thou seest me, thou seest Him,
And if thou seest Him, thou seest us both.[6]

Mansur Al Hallaj

At the basis of all beliefs is our level of awareness of our existence. How do we experience our day-to-day lives? What do we value? What is important? To help modify veterans' beliefs in the direction of Posttraumatic Growth (PTG), veterans must be able to tolerate a process of self-questioning. As therapists,

---

6 Nicholson, Reynold A. *The Mystics of Islam* (London and Boston: Routledge Kegan Paul, 1963) 151.

our role is to help veterans become aware of how their usual answers to life's difficulties interfere with overcoming those very difficulties.

The therapist does not treat the patient by simply giving him another set of beliefs. She tries to help him see which kinds of ideas and beliefs have led to his suffering. Many patients want to get rid of their painful feelings, but they do not want to get rid of their beliefs, the viewpoints that are the very roots of their feelings. So therapist and patient have to work together to help the patient see things as they are.[7]

Thich Nhat Han

Most veterans are aware that what they believe is not effective, but they lack knowledge of alternative beliefs and the necessary skills to change existing beliefs that are ineffective.

Veterans have been confronted with the reality that most of us try to avoid: the temporariness of life. However, they also try to avoid facing their temporary existence. They attempt to deny and split off the traumatic combat information from their daily lives. As a result, they experience severe emotions of sadness, grief, anger, and fear. The chaotic organization of their beliefs results in internal feelings of chaos and disorganization.

If belief systems are modified through treatment to include traumatic information in a new system of organization, then chaotic emotions diminish and new feelings of clarity, purpose, and peace begin to emerge. This modification is the basis of PTG.

---

7 Thich Nhat Han, *Peace Is Every Step* (New York: Bantam Books, 1991) 56.

Our work is to learn and to practice how to make the best of our life in the world, how to develop that strength which is necessary for us to keep firm and steady through the continual jarring influences of everyday life. How to look after the condition of our physical body, our moral upon which our life's success or failure, our happiness or unhappiness depends. It is these questions that we are concerned with, and if spirituality comes in and if God-ideal comes in, and if religion comes in, it is pertaining to this particular question: the question of how to make the best of our life?[8]

Hazrat Inayat Khan

---

8 Inayat Khan, *The Complete Works of Pir-O-Murshid Hazrat Inayat Khan, Original Texts, Lectures on Sufism, 1924 I: January - June.* (New Lebanon: Omega Publications with the Nekbkaht Foundation, 2002).

PART IV
TREATMENT

Chapter One
Treatment for Veterans of All Our Wars

Eight wars have been conducted by the United States since I was born in the early 1940s: World War II, Korea, Vietnam, Grenada, Persian Gulf, Iraq, and Afghanistan. Veterans of all those wars now seek treatment for their suffering. Because of overwhelming publicity regarding the high incidence of PTSD among combat troops, as well as articles that detail the hidden costs of wars (loss of workforce, substance abuse, increase in prison population, domestic violence, and homelessness), there has been a surge of interest in how to best treat returning veterans.

Treatment can be very direct and straightforward, if we want to simply reduce the severity of veterans' symptoms. However, the treatment I have practiced for over thirty years focuses, instead, on not just reducing the severity of symptoms, but also on actually facilitating emotional and psychological growth as a direct result of combat experiences.

Although the symptoms of PTSD remain remarkably similar across wars, they are very different in terms of floridity, or in the degree they interfere in the veteran's life, or in the degree they cause the veteran emotional distress. As veterans age, their emotional difficulties become increasingly chronic—more of a "way of living." Veterans from WWII and Korea have adjusted to their symptoms to the point where they view them as part of their lives. This does not mean that those WWII and Korea veterans are not amenable to treatment, only that treatment will be different for them than for Vietnam veterans or Iraq/Afghanistan veterans.

The type of PTG that older veterans may be directed to is expressed in the life-span psychologist Erik Erikson's descriptions of the conflict we face as we move into the final phase of our physical lives. Erikson maintained that in our final phase, we face a conflict between integrity and despair. If we can say about our lives that, "what had to be was, and it was good," then we have chosen integrity; however, if we instead choose to focus on our regrets and resentments, then we have chosen despair.[1]

Treatment of World War II Veterans: Honor and Despair

There are untold dimensions waiting for the adventurer in the inner life. WWII veterans need hope, dreams, and possibilities, just like all of us. If they can integrate their traumatic memories, a new world opens.

If WWII veterans have despair, then it is important to work with their memories of combat. Most WWII veterans have never spoken about their war activities. A good place to begin is with their military training

1 Erikson, Eric,. *Identity and The Life Cycle* (New York: W.W. Norton and Co., 1980).

and the types of relationships they formed during their military service.

Prior to working with WWII veterans, therapists need to read the book *Wartime* by Paul Fussell.[2] Because there was a cohesiveness amongst WWII veterans that is difficult to duplicate in the postmodern military, it is important to re-emphasize that cohesiveness during WWII veterans' accounts of their experiences. These veterans have rarely experienced that sort of closeness with other men ever again. They experienced the death in battle of many of their close friends, and have never forgotten those moments.

Part of their despair stems from their belief that they also should have died in the war. They struggle with why they didn't, and with self-recriminations regarding how they didn't live up to the chances they had in their lives.

Tom was eighty-six and had never discussed the war with anyone. He had come into treatment because he could no longer bear the memories alone, but did not want to "burden" his wife and children with his torment.

"You know," he told me, "I have no idea why I didn't die that day. So many people died. God, I remember the bodies and the smell. You never forget the smell. And what have I done since? What did I do with the opportunity of life? Not much! Made some money, raised some kids. I guess that was important, but they don't seem to care much. Not that I want them to make a big deal out of me. I understand. They have

2 Fussell, Paul. *Wartime: Understanding and Behavior in the Second World War* (Oxford: Oxford University Press, 1990).

their families, their lives." Tom looked slightly embarrassed to be talking so much.

"What seems important is how you feel about your life," I offered.

He looked bemused. "Sure, of course. But I feel like crap. I feel like I wasted most of my time. I didn't do what I wanted."

"What can you do now?" I wondered.

"Oh, it's too late," he said with a smile.

"Why?" I asked.

"I am eighty-six years old. I have diabetes, and a bad ticker. I am lucky to get out of bed in the morning."

"That's true. You have lived longer than most. You have experienced events that very few left alive have experienced. You have lived the best way you know how, and you can still get out of bed in the morning."

He laughed. "You know Doc, you're right. I guess I'm just feeling sorry for myself."

"Now, don't give me that crap," I said. "These are real feelings of regret for you. You need to honor them but not let them drown you. What is it that you want to do, now? Not 'what is urgent?' but 'what is important?'"

"Well, just keep getting up and saying hello to the day. But you know, going over these things [his wartime experiences] seems to be helping. I don't sit as much just thinking; instead, I talk more with my wife. Although I don't know if she likes that so much," he laughed.

Treatment of Veterans in Light of Their Spiritual Belief.

It is important to help these veterans to shift their thoughts from the past to the future, particularly in terms of spiritual ideas. If veterans are satisfied with their religion, their church, or their synagogue, perhaps they might be willing to discuss their faith. Perhaps they have come to an understanding of the war from a spiritual perspective. However, this age group generally tends to be private, and may have never discussed those beliefs. Verbalizing their spiritual beliefs and connecting them to their emotions is a powerful part of their process of finding hope and peace in their lives.

Edward was eighty-two and had experienced intense fighting in Northern Africa, then had moved on to Italy. In treatment, he described the killing. Since he had told me that he was a regular church-going Protestant, I asked him to tell me what role his religious beliefs had in his understanding of the war.

"I don't know what you mean," he answered.

"What did God have to do with the war?" I clarified.

"I don't think that God had anything to do with it, except maybe He spared my life. *We* did the war. *We* did the killing. God didn't do any of that. I give thanks every Sunday that I didn't die. Is that what you mean?"

"When you give thanks, what's that like?"

"What's that like? It's good, I feel better. But then the memories return and I feel like crap again."

"It sounds like you're taking on a lot of responsibility. Maybe God could take some of the responsibility for putting you through the war?"

"Hey, I chose to do that. I volunteered. I did what I had to do, and God didn't have anything to with it!"

"And you did your duty with honor and bravery. War is a messy experience of blood and chaos. As you said, you did what you had to do. Is it possible to appreciate yourself?"

"Yeah. But there were so many men who had it a lot tougher than I did." Then he paused and added, "I like myself. After going through what we've been doing here, I find that I feel better about what happened. All of us, we did what we had to do. It was a big mess, but we had to do it."

Treatment of Veterans Who Lack a Spiritual Belief

If the WWII veterans you encounter in treatment do not have a concept of God and have decided that there is nothing after the physical life, they still probably believe that the present life is important.

Jacob had been a pilot of a bombardier, making runs from England over Germany. His plane was shot down coming back over France. The pilot would be the last person out of the plane. In addition, his parachute was stored under his seat. When Jacob was finally able to get up, he grabbed his parachute, noticed that some of the flak from the anti-aircraft fire had penetrated the packing material, and, briefly, froze. He realized that there might be holes in his parachute that would result in his plunging to his death. He had no choice, and went out the door. The chute functioned enough that he was able to make it safely to the ground.

In our third session, Jacob tried to explain to me how he felt about existence. "What's important to me is right now. I mean, I don't really know what's going to happen after I die, but I don't believe that there's some heaven waiting—or, more likely, some hell. I just think that this deal is over and that's it."

"So there's just going to be nothing?"

"Right. It's like being asleep without any dreams. Darkness. I don't know anything, and I don't exist."

"That's why you have lived your life trying to be present for every moment. Because that's all there is."

"Yes, I'm glad you see that. It's a damn waste of time thinking about some Walt Disney heaven. What's going on here is what's important. My kids, my wife, my friends, my garden—everything I do."

Jacob was expressing a sincere belief that he had lived by. He identified with that belief, and it governed his life. His exiting the airplane with a possibly faulty parachute determined the direction he would go. That he would choose to embrace the present moment as full of life instead of resigning to the inevitability of death. The alchemy of the moment moved him into a level of nafs that was both focused and restrictive. In some ways his beliefs are close to Buddhism without the Buddhist expansiveness of possibilities.

In treating WWII veterans, work with their memories of the war, but encourage them to keep themselves in the present. How do their memories intrude? What is it like when they are caught in a memory of the war?

Most WWII veterans have believed that they should never talk about their experiences, and that if they do express them they will be violating an unspoken code among other WWII veterans. So sometimes it will be important to question their assumptions about expressing their memories.

However, they are in the therapist's office because they are no longer able to bear their memories. The therapist's active willingness to listen and be a witness to veterans' memories is not only important to the veterans themselves but also to the oral history of their generation.

PTG will take place when veterans are able to find peace in their lives and be thankful for their existence—in other words, have a sense of integrity.

Treatment of Korean War Veterans: Integrity vs. Despair

Before starting treatment with Korean War veterans, it's advisable to read the book, *Breakout: The Chosin Reservoir Campaign*, by Martin Russ,[3] to get a sense of the Korean War.

Korean War veterans are in their late seventies to early eighties. Many of these veterans experienced human wave attacks, as the North Korean Army and Chinese advisors attacked their positions.

Ralph was in his late seventies and had been a machine gunner in Korea. His life after the war had been a series of part-time jobs and long periods of alcoholic hazes. He had been sober for about ten years when he began having hallucinations about his friends who had died in Korea. He began seeing them on the streets and would go over to them, but they would suddenly disappear.

In treatment, after telling me about the hallucinations, Ralph asked, with a grin, "Are you going to lock me up and call the guys in the white coats? Do you think I'm crazy?"

I replied, "No, I don't think you are crazy. I think you are very sad about having lost your friends. I

---

3 Russ, Martin. *Breakout: The Choisin Reservoir Campaign* (New York: Penguin, 2000).

think you probably need to say a proper goodbye to them."

Ralph looked at me, "How do I do that, Doc?"

"Can you think of them as being here now?"

"Well, I don't like the feeling of seeing them. Isn't there another way of doing it?"

"OK. When you see them on the street, say to them quietly, 'Goodbye.' Then tell me how that goes."

Ralph's resistance to the alchemical action of Korea had resulted in his calcinatio, the frozen state when the dragon escapes, producing images from his past in order to break through his fixation. Because of his open-heartedness, his nafs, although still disorganized, had shown him how to care for others. However, his torment over the killing did not allow him to identify with his new beliefs. He believed that it was a good thing to care about other people, but he did not believe that he was sufficiently adequate in his caring. His actions in Korea convinced him that he was an inherently evil person who could commit horrible acts that would shock everyone except other veterans. His hallucinations were a result of the emergence of his ideal self as his psyche insisted that he form a greater self-concept.

Treatment of Vietnam Veterans: Dignity and Confusion

Veterans from Vietnam are in late middle age and entering their senior years. While they may still struggle with florid symptoms that interfere with their daily lives, they also may have adopted lifestyles that allow them to maintain at least a semblance of effective functioning. Vietnam veterans are still in turmoil, alternately experiencing solve and the calcinatio as they cycle through falling apart and forcing themselves to hold it together.

They have entered their late fifties and early sixties with some surprise that they are still amongst the living. Now, they must solve their issues of remorse, guilt, anger, and acceptance. In Erikson's levels of ego development,[4] Vietnam veterans are struggling with either continuing to be productive or stagnating (e.g., falling asleep in front of the TV during the day). These veterans are most amenable to the full program of exposure treatment.

Exposure Treatment

Exposure treatment involves a detailed remembering and retelling of the traumas.

It is important for therapists to begin exposure treatment only after they feel that the veteran has been able to master the appropriate coping skills, and that a sufficient rapport has been established. This model of exposure treatment begins with childhood as a way of reminding veterans of their innocence and providing a safe place when the memories of trauma become overwhelming.

Childhood: The interaction between the soul and the material world. Childhood can be a time of innocence and safety.

However, it is frequently the opposite: parents unskilled in the art of parenting can deliver all kinds of physical, sexual, and emotional abuse. Many veterans had childhoods filled with abuse, and so it is

---

4 Erikson, Erik. *Identity and The Life Cycle*, (New York: W.W. Norton and Co., 1980).

important to help them sort out their emotions and thoughts regarding their parents' actions, in part, because this early trauma tends to make veterans more emotionally susceptible to later trauma.

The majority of veterans I have treated over the last thirty years, however, have had positive childhood experiences with parents who attempted to perform to the best of their abilities.

If veterans in treatment did experience a positive childhood, therapists can help them to establish a sense of safety and a way of remembering positive regard for others. The experience of caring, compassionate teachers during elementary school years is more common than not. And the experience of bonding with other children and having months filled with the joy of childhood exploration can be seen (when looked into) as taking up more internal space than the horror stories of abuse.

Regardless of whether childhood was abusive or nurturing, it's important that therapists spend time helping veterans remember their innocence. This phase was the beginning of the development of the nafs; and it is helpful to learn how the nafs of the adult has not only been influenced by the trauma of war, but also by the experiences of childhood.

The mystical view of childhood sees it as the emergence of the interaction between the soul and the material world—the alchemical materialization of spirit.

In addition to other healing benefits, this phase of treatment also allows a deeper rapport to develop between therapist and veterans.

The Vietnam Generation:
The Cultural Impact on Treatment

The Vietnam War involved and polarized the country. The polarization influenced the Vietnam veteran possibly as much as did the traumas of combat. The conflicts of WWII and the Korean War (officially termed a "Police Action") had been seen as necessary wars, but Vietnam was not accepted in the same way. There was a wide resistance to conscription by a large portion of draft age men. Draftees/soldiers are necessarily young. Young men can be trained to obey suicidal orders. The older we become the more we question the authority of those ordering us.

During adolescence, an important part of our lives' development occurred: the dawning of transitional understanding. We realized that eventually we were going to move into adulthood and would have to take responsibility for ourselves. But we also wanted to continue our childhood, with its freedom from responsibility, yet at the same time explore our new physical sensations. Adolescence is a period of powerful conflicting impulses, and a structuring of a level of nafs that is mostly the commanding self. During this stage of life, many young men and women viewed the military as providing a structure for those conflicts.

The link between adolescence and U.S. cultural history during the Vietnam War. During the Vietnam War, the country was consumed by a cultural opening to different perspectives on reality. Those perspectives, along with inspiring an enormous involvement in spiritual mysticism, tragically and paradoxically, also created one of the most difficult experiences for the returning soldiers—and "Sanctuary Trauma" was created.

However, this cultural impact was also felt by therapists who formed the beginning of effective treatment of combat trauma. In Gerald Nicosia's book *Home to War*, he states, "According to Robert Lifton, there was a separate war among the shrinks. As the rap groups progressed, a number of the professionals found themselves growing very uneasy with the kind of parity between doctors and 'patients' that the veterans were demanding."[5] Veterans were not accepting the sense of being "one down" in treatment. They pointed out that therapists did not understand the effects of combat and veterans' role was to teach as well as to be treated.

As a result of the "parity," Vietnam veterans demanded the creation of a program to treat PTSD. As a result of these demands, the Readjustment Counseling Service (also known as "The Vet Centers") was formed within the Department of Veterans Affairs—the first government-funded program to specifically provide psychotherapy for combat veterans (treatment for PTSD).

In the culture, more liberal values had begun to take place among younger persons. A greater acceptance of a variety of physical appearances (e.g., long hair and beards) was the superficial expression of a greater permissiveness. As a result of mass public higher education, exploration of existential meaning

---

5 Nicosia, Gerald. *Home to War: A History of the Vietnam Veterans' Movement*, (New York: Crown, 2001).

had reached the middle class. Along with questioning the materialism of the 1950s, middle class youths challenged authority, in particular condemning the government's use of military conscription. The term "sanctuary trauma" refers to veterans' experience of being rejected and vilified by the country when they returned from war. This sanctuary trauma is brilliantly portrayed in Nicosia's *Home to War*.[6]

Opposition to the war was fueled by many variables, but the most prominent was the military draft. The draft probably resulted in more college degrees than any other single factor. If you were in college and maintained a certain level of academic units, you were granted a college deferment.

The college deferment added to some veterans' later beliefs that they had been duped and tricked into going to war. It told them that the government valued a college degree over military service in Vietnam. It seemed clear to many veterans, after the war, that going willingly into the military had been a mistake.

Of course, there were many young men and women who believed that they had a duty to protect the country, and as veterans they continue to profess that belief over forty years later. In their reasoning, they would rather fight the communists in Southeast Asia than on the streets of America, and that if South Vietnam were to become communist then so would Cambodia, Thailand, Indonesia, etc.

But many of the young men and women who volunteered for military service at that time simply were interested in acquiring structure and purpose to their

---

6 Nicosia, Gerald, *Home to War: A History of the Vietnam Veterans' Movement* (New York: Carroll and Graf, 2004).

lives. They were not interested in the world of academia (not yet, at least), and the available jobs were boring compared to the adventure of war.

The role of politics is overrated when applied to why young people are willing to go to war. The vast majority of soldiers do not care about the politics. They are interested in testing themselves in terms of their physical endurance and in their courage to face death.

Duty, honor, service, and self-sacrifice are inspiring qualities to individuals of any age and gender. Regardless of whether the war is an unabashed invasion of a sovereign nation or interference in a divided country's attempt at self-determination, the view is that it is their patriotic duty to support the war.

Due to these and many more motivations, young men and women entered the military, served honorably in their tour of duty in Vietnam, and returned to a changed country. In the earlier stages of the war (1965-1968), veterans left a country that was in a transitional period, culturally, and returned to an almost unrecognizable atmosphere. Their "Welcome Home" was the shock of physical appearances of their peer group, drug use, liberal sex, and a sometimes violently expressed hatred of everything military.

Soldiers' return from Vietnam was determined by DEROS (Date of Expected Return from Over Seas), unless they had received a serious wound. In later years the Vietnamese military would cite DEROS as a major reason for the lack of morale in American troops. The Americans' tour of duty in Vietnam was for one year (for Marines it was thirteen months).

Many veterans, experiencing the devastating sanctuary trauma once back in the U.S., immediately requested a return to the war zone.

Veterans had spent many months trying to escape from their situation while in the war zone by indulging in fantasies about what their return to civilian life would be like. When the society's rejection became all too real, they once again retreated into fantasy. Coping with stress through fantasy is a theme among combat veterans of *all* wars. The soldiers' reality was so aversive that they attempted to avoid that reality through constant fantasizing about going home.

For Vietnam veterans, sanctuary trauma was not just about culture shock, disappointed fantasies, and rejection from their peers. It was also about rejection from older veterans.

When I and others first started the Vet Center in Santa Barbara, I would speak to the local veteran service groups, such as the VFW, American Legion, and Disabled Veterans of America. I would begin the talk with a short description of PTSD, and then would have a Vietnam veteran get up and talk about how the war had affected him. That is, I gave the psychological perspective, and the veteran gave a first-person account of PTSD.

At one such presentation, something unusual, but perhaps to be expected, happened. Santa Barbara has a beautiful waterfront, and there was a veterans' hall right on the beach—a gorgeous setting, with blue sky and a sparkling ocean. My talk, given in a large hall in the veterans' building, was well attended by many older veterans. These men were obviously used to each other and showed a lot of camaraderie as they settled into their lunch. After their meal, the president of the group introduced me. The men grew silent and seemed to be attentive. However, throughout my talk they became increasingly restless and showed some real signs of uneasiness.

When I had finished, I introduced the Vietnam veteran who had accompanied me—a former Marine who had received a Combat Action Ribbon and a Purple Heart. He took the podium and began to speak. Now the room was very quiet as he began to describe some of the conflicts he had experienced.

Suddenly, in the back of the room, an older man stood up and said, "Hey, I think that's just about enough of that. OK. You saw some action. So what? Some of our battles probably lasted longer than your tour of duty. And we don't talk about it and you shouldn't either!" With that, he turned and left.

Now the room was completely still. The Marine at the podium looked at the other veterans and said, "That's why I am here today. I don't want to be like that. When I get to your age I don't want to have these memories continue to destroy me." The Marine went on to describe his combat and his symptoms of PTSD. When he finished, the audience rose almost as one and gave him a thundering standing ovation.

The younger and outspoken Vietnam veterans seemed to offend the older generation. That offense resulted in further rejection of Vietnam veterans; and for many years, Vietnam veterans were not allowed in the American Legion and Veterans of Foreign Wars. Now, with an aging population and a realization of past mistakes, those organizations welcome Vietnam veterans and even actively solicit their membership.

Veterans of Southeast Asia were often mistreated by the military. Vietnam veterans were famously not impressed by rank, based on their experience in the jungles and rice paddies when their officers would make serious mistakes that cost lives. So it's not surprising that Vietnam veterans often lost respect for command. But the military is famous for not understanding these attitudes; and many dishonorable discharges were the result of the stateside military coming into confrontation with combat veterans.

All this happened many years ago. Between then and now, Vietnam veterans may have had several jobs, several marriages, substance abuse, and possibly violent interactions with others. Now they are older but still struggling with many symptoms of PTSD. Time does not heal PTSD. It simply distracts from it.

Vietnam veterans have reached a time in life when their regular defenses are no longer adequate. They cannot continue to distract themselves with TV, drugs, alcohol, sex, work, school, mind-pursuits, and other more idiosyncratic methods. Now their symptoms are becoming more disturbing, and many of them have become seriously concerned about their mental and emotional health.

They usually don't expect therapists to be able to help them. They mostly come to therapists as a last resort. They find it embarrassing to seek treatment.

Dealing With Shame: The Need For Control

The shame of seeking treatment for an emotional disorder is common among men in general. Most definitions of shame refer to the individual's sense of inadequacy or exposure, in which the sense of self is in danger of being flooded or overwhelmed with negative feelings about the self. Women are generally seen as shame-prone, but men are seen as shame-vulnerable. That is, for men, feelings of shame are not acceptable, although they are intrinsic in our culture. For women, feelings of shame are just one of many emotions in their repertoire that are culturally acceptable.

When men experience shame, they connect to a belief of original sin; they feel innately flawed. Shame is devastating to their sense of self, and they actively defend against the experience. Most male veterans would prefer being angry to feeling shame.

Shame is different from guilt. Guilt has to do with having done something we regret: for example, an action we expressed that violated our sense of ethics or morals produces feelings of guilt. In this way guilt can be an appropriate, even helpful, emotion that helps us to not repeat an action.

Many survivors of combat wonder why they survived and others did not. The survivors often compare their sense of self with their impression of those who were killed. The survivors often feel lacking in that comparison and suffer what is commonly termed "survivor guilt." But it is neither survivor guilt nor survivor shame that veterans experience in regards to surviving war. Unless they did something that they perceived as being cowardly, their survival is not experienced as guilt. In addition, shame is not an appropriate label unless the survivor feels innately flawed. While veterans may feel guilt in terms of some of their actions, they do not feel shame unless they believe they have been "born bad." Perhaps the proper term for so-called survivor guilt would be "survivor confusion." Survivor confusion is a complete astonishment at having survived, and not understanding why.

Shame is a debilitating emotion that creates hopelessness and despair. It interferes with moving forward in emotional development, causing the belief that we will never be adequate. Because we see ourselves as innately flawed, we feel that we are not able—and never will be able—to progress with our awareness and effectiveness. Regardless of how well we accomplish and how much we achieve, there is always the underlying hurt of our shame.

These very male attitudes and ideas regarding shame seriously limit most men in disclosing their private selves. They grow into adulthood emotionally disconnected from significant experiences in their lives and socially isolated. Including such experiences as war in their development only increases their emotional restriction.

The very act of seeking treatment is itself humiliating for men, and even more so for veterans. It is a public admission that they can't do it by themselves; that they need someone else's help.

Setting Up Treatment

In order to combat the feelings of shame, veterans must experience a sense of control in the treatment sessions—particularly within the context of the treatment plan.

It is important to outline the treatment plan to the veteran prior to beginning treatment. Veterans need to know that they have a right to withdraw, to refuse to discuss certain experiences, and to terminate treatment. Almost all individuals with PTSD struggle with control issues; and the therapist's recognition of this as a major issue for combat veterans is important in establishing rapport.

Therapists might also think about the physical arrangement of the office. When men talk to each other, they primarily stand side by side. They may face each other at an angle if they are attempting to communicate something important. However, when they face each other directly—look at each other eye-to-eye—they view this as either of two possibilities: one, there is going to be physical violence; or two, one man is giving orders to the other man. Therefore, the therapy room should be arranged so that while there is eye contact, there is not a threatening atmosphere.

Many women rejected Vietnam veterans when these men returned home. Women (and men) spit on them, threw things at them, and called them names. As a result of that rejection, and veterans' general belief that it's best to remain silent about their combat experiences in the presence of civilians, Vietnam veterans have rarely confided in women—including wives, girl friends, and significant others—regarding their actions in Vietnam.

The young Marine lieutenant was traveling to New York via train from Washington D.C., where he had received the nation's second highest honor, the Navy Cross, for his heroism in leading his Marines up a hill against overwhelming North Vietnamese machine gunners. He was traveling in his uniform with the medal and his service ribbons on his jacket. As he sat in his seat he watched a very beautiful young woman begin to walk up the aisle. She smiled at him as she approached his seat. He returned the smile. Then her face changed, she spit on him, and uttered the dumbest of phrases, "Baby killer!"

However, as veterans age and become more open to the feminine perspective (some research asserts that as men age they begin to reach out more to women as friends other than simply physical partners) regarding their nightmares and intrusive thoughts, they become more accepting of women and more respectful of women's insights. Veterans hope that the feminine nature can heal and nurture them. They will even admit their failed relationships, shame, and guilt, so that women can forgive them and help elevate their status to that of a warrior.

Veterans would like a warrior culture that will support them and give them a sense of pride in their combat actions.

If childhood has been adequately processed, these issues of shame and guilt may subside for a time. However, shame and guilt may return even more intensely as treatment proceeds. If the therapeutic relationship has been adequately developed this is a great opportunity to heal a chronic and difficult belief. Therapist openness and interest helps veterans express their pain and develop alternative perspectives.

Military training

Vietnam veterans can be classified in terms of either those who joined the military voluntarily or those who were drafted. Those who joined are termed, by the military, the "regular army." Draftees had a different attitude than the regulars, frequently feeling very reluctant regarding military service. However, once both groups graduated from boot camp or basic training, it became difficult to discern any significant differences between them in their attitudes regarding the war.

Basic training in the U. S. military is an extremely effective approach to producing warriors. It doesn't seem to matter how reluctant individuals were prior to basic training or boot camp, or whether they got there through being drafted or through joining. Military training is so effective that most individuals remember it with a great deal of pride—as young men being trained to be soldiers, obey orders, learn how to kill, and develop skills apart from those required in civilian life.

As veterans, however, they have never discussed their military training. No one, including other soldiers, has ever asked them about it.

Countless movies and books have portrayed basic training, particularly boot camp. But watching those movies is very different than actually experiencing the brutality of the drill instructor in person, and succeeding in the face of difficult physical challenges.[7]

In treatment, most veterans will attempt to skim over this part. But an exploration of their feelings about basic training is crucial to success in later phases of the treatment.

This is the beginning of the alchemical solve, the breakdown of beliefs. Their exposure to the training begins as early as the induction center. Therefore, it's

7 If you find movies helpful, then watch *Full Metal Jacket*, a movie about Marine Boot Camp during the Vietnam War.

important to discuss with veterans what the arrival was like.

Induction-center arrival. Jeff had been drafted, and his induction physical had taken place at the Los Angeles' induction center. In treatment, I asked him how he got to the center. He replied, "I took the bus from Fullerton. I was living in Buena Park, and my girl friend took me to the bus station."

"Tell me about the bus ride," I encouraged him.

"I don't really remember. That was a long time ago. I didn't know anyone, and I don't think anybody talked to me."

My intention, therapeutically, was to set the stage for the exposure—the retelling in detail of the traumas. It is important for veterans to get used to remembering the military as vividly as possible.

"What was the induction center like?" I continued.

"A big building. Oh yeah—I remember they had different colored lines you were supposed to follow. I just went through it with all of the other guys."

"What happened after the physical?"

"They put us on a bus and we went to Fort Ord."

Basic training. It's important to find out what happened when the veteran arrived at the camp as a draftee. Many veterans' stories are filled with the sudden, and frequently violent, yelling and screaming of the drill instructor. Bodies being pushed and shoved, papers being tossed and thrown, and complete intimidation are all hallmarks of arrival. The obligatory shearing haircut, the stripping of individuality, and frequent humiliation are essential ingredients of the training.

Another telling detail is how the recruit was awakened the next morning. Generally, it was by a trashcan being thrown down the aisle by the drill sergeant, accompanied by a new day of screaming and general attempts to completely terrify recruits. The recruits have only minutes to attend to basic needs such as the toilet. There is a complete, and hostile, forced intimacy with strangers. While recruits are doing their morning's business, in a stall with no door, there is a line of other recruits staring directly at them with dazed and hostile looks. The longer recruits take, the less time the other recruits have for their turn.

Morning exercises included singling out the obviously out-of-shape recruits. Usually, the weakest link was quickly spotted and targeted as a possibility for the "recycled squad." "Recycling" was for individuals who were unable to successfully complete basic training. They then were recycled through another session of basic training, this time with even more severe and punishing conditions.

Because of this kind of pain, humiliation, and trauma, veterans may not volunteer how they fared in basic training, other than in very general terms. This is why the focus on basic training is the beginning of exposure treatment.

This is an opportunity for veterans to feel emotions that they were unable to feel at the time. Successful recruits did not allow themselves awareness of feelings of anger, despair, and sadness.

Basic training produced a change from innocence to a façade of military toughness, readiness, and competence. During treatment, as veterans relive their basic training and boot camp experiences, it is important for them to also remember that crucial time of change. It was a beginning of alchemy: the pounding heat of the drill instructor; recruits' own fear of punishment; their longing to succeed, and their aspiration to ideals—all these, together, created a breakdown of adolescent ego structures. The military's purpose is to create soldiers, after all: individuals who are willing to kill and die for each other. After breaking down the recruits' egos, the military then attempts to rebuild recruits into a unified force with a willingness to sacrifice individual egos for a group purpose.

In basic training, a sense of camaraderie developed among the recruits. The realization was forcefully driven home that the entire squad had to pull together to become successful. For example, punishing the entire squad for one recruit's mistake made the point that if one individual does not perform his or her duty, everyone might suffer.

If veterans are hesitant to discuss basic training other than very briefly, ask questions. "How did you do in the marching?" "What was the obstacle course like?" "Tell me about the rifle range." "What level was your qualification?" "Were there any accidents during the grenade throwing?" "Tell me about the gas mask." "How did you do in the pugil sticks (large rods with canvas covered rubber on both ends)?"

Interpersonal interactions among the recruits were essential to the training experience. Ask about "blanket parties." Did they get into fights? Some veterans were sexually assaulted by other, more dominant, males, and suffer from extreme shame.

Sam told me about his experience at Marine boot camp in 1967. When his barracks underwent inspection, Sam would position himself as close to his bunk as possible (these were double bunks, like bunk beds). He knew that the drill instructor would hit him, and that if he wasn't able to grab the bunk he would bounce off it and get hit again.

Generally, Army soldiers and Marines had very similar basic/boot training, regardless of what Marines tell us. The Navy was somewhat less intense. However, those recruits destined for the "brown water Navy," the Riverine Force, had a particularly painful and torturous final training challenge. Part of this Riverine Force was the swift boat group made famous in the 2005 U.S. presidential elections with John Kerry. Everyone in this force had to go through a prisoner-of-war training.

Prisoner-of-war training: The prisoner-of-war training used a simulated capture of prisoners. Recruits were set loose on an island and attempted to avoid being captured by the training forces. If the recruit was able to enter a compound without detection, he was free, and moved into the next level of training. However, almost no one actually avoided capture. Those captured were held in small cages, routinely physically assaulted, and treated as prisoners-of-war. As a final stage, the recruit/prisoner was put into a very small cage that required the recruit to fold up into the fetal position. Recruits were held in the cage for twenty-four hours, unable to stretch, and in extreme pain. Most veterans rate this experience as their worst experience in the military—even more traumatic than actual combat.

Graduation: In addition to processing all this, it also is important for veterans to process the graduation. Frequently parents, friends, and siblings came to witness the graduation. Most veterans have a great deal of pride in accomplishing this transition from recruit to soldier.

Advanced training. Most soldiers then went on to advanced infantry training. However, some veterans wanted more specialized training, and elected for Special Forces, Ranger School, Airborne, SEAL Team, and Medic/Corpsman. The reasons for choosing this more elite training are many and varied. People who join the military need to test themselves; many soldiers wanted the best training possible, for their own safety; and in military culture, individuals with specialized training had a higher status.

SEAL training is especially highly regarded, and Allen had been very successful in the training. When I asked him how he had survived so well, he replied, "I put myself in the mind set that I liked it. The physical pain, being awake for days, cold water, competing against others—all of that, I really liked. I mean, it was tough, but that was what I wanted."

Allen had found that the mastery of the body could be done by the mind. But could he master his mind? He was able to develop the attitude that allowed him to physically train, he was able to focus his thoughts when on a mission; but outside of the military, his thoughts were so focused on killing that he became difficult in his relationships.

Veterans are intrigued with being able to control their thoughts; but at this point in treatment, it is too

early to attempt anything other than the most elementary of concentration exercises.

> *...[C]ontrol of the thoughts ... is the second step, con-
> trol of the body coming first. Thousands of people
> have found that they can sit in the postures for hours,
> but cannot keep their mind still. This has to be learned
> by degrees. A person cannot control his mind by willing
> to think of nothing; that will never be possible. First let
> the mind hold whatever thought interests it, any thought
> of love, of goodwill—whatever interests it. Check its ten-
> dency to jump from one thing to another. When you
> catch the mind jumping from one thing to another,
> bring it back and hold it. You must say: I am greater
> than my mind, my will is greater than my mind, and I
> will make my mind obey my will.*[8]

Hazrat Inayat Khan

**Concentration II: A Practice to Increase Mental
Concentration.** This is similar to the earlier exercise
in concentration: "Concentration I: A Practice to
Reduce Agitation."

Ask veterans to close their eyes. Have them visually
form a circle of light, like a spotlight. They can make
the circle of light larger and smaller, closer and far-
ther away. As they become more proficient, they will
feel more confident with moving and changing the
light. Along with aiding in the focus of thoughts this
begins to relax the mind. It also provides a possible
experience of something beyond the physical.

8 Inayat Khan, *Spiritual Liberty*, *The Sufi Message* series *Vol.
XIII* (Geneva: International Headquartersl Sufi Movement,
1991).

Veterans who served in the Rangers, etc., have pride in having succeeded at elite forces' training. However, that training also changed some aspects of their humanity.

Most grunts/infantrymen were traumatized in the war by the killing of women and children. Even when the child might have had a grenade and would have killed the veteran, it is still an action that haunts the ordinary soldier. However, the elite forces' training apparently is able to submerge that part of the individual that has compassion for innocence.

The elite forces seem to be without compassion, except for other team members. The major trauma for a SEAL is not the killing of a child but a disruption in the team. If a SEAL team member is ostracized by other team members, the traumatic effects are similar to the grunt's agonized guilt over the killing of a child.

Army medics' and Navy corpsmen's training is highly specialized. In Special Forces medics' training, they learn how to dress combat wounds by using goats. Initially Special Forces used dogs, but enough dog owners in the Army objected; so goats were substituted.

In their training Special Forces medics first of all remove the goat's spleen. The goat must survive this operation and all of what's to come, or the medic must start over with a new goat. After removing the spleen, the medic shoots the goat, attends to the wound, and makes sure the goat survives. Finally, the medic kills the goat, barbecues it, and eats it.

This training of soldiers is extremely effective in producing an organized, disciplined, killing force. Some statistics of previous wars lend credence to the effectiveness of modern training. In the United States' Civil War, the rate of return fire (the frequency of soldiers firing back when being fired upon) was only about twenty percent. This wasn't much better in WWI, where it was twenty-five percent. In WWII, the rate of return fire went up to thirty-five percent, and to forty-five percent in Korea. However, in Vietnam there was a one hundred percent rate. In fact, the soldiers had to frequently be ordered to stop firing.

Part of this enormous rate increase was the availability of ammunition. However, the training of soldiers is also a critical variable.

What was it about the training that enabled soldiers to increase their apparent effectiveness? One was the almost complete dehumanization of the enemy. This dehumanization is common to all wars, but was very effective in Vietnam. "Charlie" was no longer a person. He was a subhuman evil form who had to be killed. The Viet Cong (VC) lived up to this reputation, torturing and mutilating the soldiers they captured. The Army of the Republic of Vietnam (ARVNs), our supposed friends, were also universally hated for their obvious reluctance to engage the VC or the North Vietnamese Army (NVA). However, most soldiers express a definite admiration for the NVA regarding their discipline and willingness to fight.

In Lawrence LeShan's excellent book, *The Psychology of War*, he says, "In the mythic reality, force is ultimately the answer. The evil people are, by definition, totally evil and not redeemable by reason or sentiment."[9]

---

9 LeShan, Lawrence, *The Psychology of War: Comprehending Its Mystique and Its Madness* (Chicago: Noble Press, 1992).

Although many soldiers saw through the dehumanization process, there were also many who succumbed, and who still harbor extreme animosity towards anything Vietnamese. Studies indicate that veterans who fully adopted this sense of dehumanization have the most severe PTSD.

Perhaps the more significant variable in the training is the indoctrination that it is the "mission, not the men" that matters. Soldiers are trained not to think of their own safety, but instead to sacrifice themselves at a moment's notice for the good of the group. The ideals of honor, bravery, and self-sacrifice are drilled into the recruits from the moment they descend from the bus at the training center.

Comparability to the mystic's training. The training of the mystic is similar in some ways to the training of soldiers, in terms of the discipline necessary for the constant repetition of prayers, meditation, and sacred phrases. LeShan notes:

As human beings we have fundamental needs both for a strong sense of our own individuality and sharp vividness of experience, and also for the knowledge that we are an integral and accepted part of a group, of something larger than ourselves. Outside of the esoteric spiritual-development schools, limited to only a comparatively few followers because of the long, hard discipline they demand, only war promises to fulfill both needs at the same time.[10]

Young, impressionable minds are hungry for anything that will inspire and lead them into what promises to be the ultimate test of their abilities. When our culture

10 Ibid., 88.

is so shallow that the idea of traveling to a foreign land for the purpose of killing other warriors is the most meaningful option for young people, it is important to reconsider our cultural and personal values.

Regaining idealism. As a nation, we seem to exist moving between the lower nafs, generally inhabiting and transitioning between the commanding self and self-accusing levels. A set of very high ideals, beyond those nafs, is instilled in young men and women during military basic training—ideals that touch them in a deeper, more profound manner than do other aspects of our culture. However, that training does not work towards the fulfillment of those high ideals, instead being directed towards killing other human beings in the name of service to the country.

Basic training challenges young people not only physically but also mentally and emotionally. *Esprit de corps* is a major aspect of all early military training. The acceptance of the mission and the willingness to sacrifice individual lives is basic to this esprit. Similar to fundamentalist religions, the military's basic training sets up life as black-and-white, as us-versus-them. In so doing, it gives a sense of belonging and direction to young people whose culture has offered them only the emptiness of materialism.

However, the insubstantiality of those military ideals is soon realized by soldiers returning from war. Betrayed by officers and the military, and summarily discharged, veterans are left with nightmares, depression, and panic attacks.

One door into veterans' healing is that, as soldiers, they believed in those military ideals. So in treatment, therapists help veterans to remember those beliefs so that they can look back at that time and regain their idealism. It is important to help veterans honor those ideals regardless of the actions of the military, as those ideals stimulated a genuine awareness of a larger purpose and wholeness.

This reflection on the greater good is necessary in order for veterans to be psychologically prepared to enter into the traumatic material of the theater of operations (the war zone) within the treatment. The purpose of treatment is to help veterans expand their belief systems so they can better integrate the traumatic information and gain a deeper understanding of existence. This is what moves them towards Posttraumatic Growth.

Therefore, it is important for therapists to generally refrain from asking veterans *feeling* questions ("How are you feeling?"), and, instead, to periodically ask, "How are you? What is this like for you? What is it like to talk about this?" These kinds of questions frequently enable veterans to directly relate, usually in physical-allusive language: "I'm getting really jacked up." "I'm all jittery inside." "I don't like this, I'm getting too wound up." These answers are exceptionally revealing of the veteran's inner world, and are cautionary statements, requesting a slowing down of the exposure. However, after moving through exposure treatment focused on basic training, veterans are usually ready to move to the next phase and responds to inquiries about their inner experience with positive statements.

Returning to the theater of operations. At this point in treatment, veterans are involved in the process, and most resistance to memories has diminished. Arriving in the war zone (Vietnam, Kuwait, Afghanistan, etc.) is an event not just of crossing geographical borders but also of crossing a psychological border. There is an inner change when we become fully a part of a force of people who are directed at killing other people.

Louis had decided to enlist because he felt a strong patriotic duty. After excelling in basic training he wanted more advanced training, so he opted for jump school. After his successes there, he went to Vietnam.

I asked him, "What was it like when your orders came through?"

"It was great," he replied. "I was finally going to do something for my country."

"Where did you disembark from, and how did you get to Vietnam?" I asked.

Louis described the plane flight, its stopover in Hawaii, and its final landing in Da Nang.

"What's the first thing you remember when you got off the plane?"

"The heat and the smell."

"Describe it to me," I requested.

"The heat was overwhelming. I grew up in Tucson, but this heat was completely different. I started sweating and I don't think I ever stopped. And the smells were just the smells of a different culture, and of course the jungle. Oh yeah—there was also the smell of burning shit." (The military disposed of their solid human waste by pouring gasoline on it and burning it.)

Deployment: realization of mortality. Soldiers become veterans when they enter the war zone; and at some point the war becomes real (usually when a mortar round lands or a round goes hissing by), and individuals change.

I've had veterans tell me of the shock they experienced when they realized that a complete stranger was shooting at them. Veterans say, "I wanted to find [the shooter] and tell him that I was a good guy. I couldn't believe that someone I didn't even know was trying to kill me."

Another moment of reality comes when someone in the squad is killed or wounded. Most young people feel immortal and don't believe that they can be killed. That myth is shattered when soldiers see the dead and wounded. In treatment, it is important for veterans to remember this moment and re-experience the emotions.

Soldiers' realization of their own mortality widened their belief systems suddenly; and when the information proved too nerve-wracking, it rebounded and contracted. Suddenly realizing that you could die at any moment immediately widens your ideas about life. You understand more fully how temporary we are. But your sense of temporariness contracts into wanting to extend the length of time. This widening and contraction became a theme that stayed with soldiers throughout their tours of duty. It was like having a sudden insight about life that is so overwhelming that the mind cannot grasp it, and the insight therefore is banished to the unconscious.

For this phase—the realization of one's mortality— to proceed smoothly in treatment, it's important to know terms unique to the war. Therapists thus can ask veterans to explain them. While veterans may enjoy teaching therapists about the terms of war to some extent, it is also helpful if therapists can demonstrate some background and experience on their own. For this reason, some of the terms used in the Vietnam and Iraq wars are listed in the glossary.

Means of deployment. Vietnam veterans usually went to Vietnam by plane, but a significant minority went by ship. (Bear in mind that a ship is big, while a boat is smaller.)

For veterans who were deployed by ship, it is important to discuss this. The conditions were usually stark and difficult. Stories abound about trashcans full of vomit from the innumerable seasick soldiers. The bunks (racks) were usually hammocks strung four up. Many times, individuals in the top racks were prone to enuresis; (bed-wetting)—unfortunately for the men in the lower racks, as they were the recipients of that waste. In addition, one can only imagine the utter boredom and despair the young soldiers experienced en route to war.

Arriving in Vietnam by ship may have required soldiers to deploy via a beach landing. Many times the landing itself was as if going into hostile fire, and sometimes there actually were hostilities. Mostly, after climbing precariously into a landing craft, they were deposited on a beach where there was a waiting bus or deuce and a half (a large transport vehicle) to transport them to their staging area.

The majority of men, however, arrived by plane. The Marines went through Taiwan, famous for its saloons and whorehouses.

It is important to help veterans maintain a *sensory* connection to their memories. Otherwise their recollections are in danger of becoming just another story, with their tellers so detached that it is as if they are watching a movie.

For treatment to work, the veteran must agree, at least tacitly, to return to Vietnam or whatever was their theater of operations. During the work with coping skills, this return must be emphasized as their reason to learn those skills. But veterans must also maintain a connection with the present and with the awareness of their current safety.

They get off the plane. Where do they go? Remember they do not yet have a weapon. Ask them, "Did you have a weapon?" This continues to orient them to the experience of Vietnam. The emotional quality of not having a weapon in a war zone is part of the beginning of Vietnam for veterans. In addition, veterans are very knowledgeable about all kinds of weapons, and it helps to give them the opportunity to describe their weapons.

Weapons. They are transported to a base, given weapons (what kind?), and other gear (canteens, etc.). Ask them, "What did the weapons feel like? What did you think of them?" For example, the M16 was generally hated by the earlier troops (1967–1970) when it replaced the M14. The M16 rifle tended to easily jam, misfire, and lack the power the soldiers associated with the M14.

Their weapons and their firepower kept soldiers alive. The better veterans understood how the weapons worked, the more effectively they could repair and clean those weapons in the field.

Veterans may retain this curiosity and interest in weapons, even though it was initially spurred by life-and-death struggles. Many veterans have since completely rejected all types of weapons, and have not held a rifle since the military. But there are also veterans with huge gun collections (e.g., 360 assorted guns) and an almost obsessive fascination with weapons of all kinds.

Regardless of veterans' current feelings regarding weapons, it is important to help them discuss their own weapons. Soldiers in the special forces, rangers, SEALs, some special squads, and other specially trained forces had more esoteric weapons. These veterans are helped by being invited to discuss their weapon preferences, their idiosyncratic reasons for their preferences, and how they carried the weapon. Harold was in a special team that cleared landing zones before the infantry landed. He had modified his M16 so that he could quickly flip banana clips (clips of rounds shaped somewhat like a banana), and he had two clips taped together for quick reloading.

Weapons were always within arm's reach, and in all wars there are many accounts of soldiers suddenly being without them. Indeed, many of veterans' nightmares are centered on weapons malfunction, loss of weapons, ineffectiveness of weapons, and weapons being turned against them.

These dreams are powerful messages from the psyche, indicating veterans' need to realize their reliance on the mechanical and illusory nature of the lower self.

Base of operations. Where was the base of operations? It is quite valuable for therapists to have a good, accurate map of Vietnam, including the location of the military bases. In this way, therapists might show veterans the map and ask them to point out the location of their base and other significant areas. Although many veterans spent most of their time in the field and have only vague ideas regarding their location, all veterans had a base of operations. A good map will have that base.

Ask veterans to describe the base. Not just what it looked like, but also the smells and sounds. If they have photos, ask them to bring those pictures to the session. Pictures are powerful devices for stimulating memories. For veterans, these pictures are filled with sensory and emotional memories. When they see the pictures, they hear, feel, smell, and taste memories.

Occupational specialties (MOS). What were veterans' military occupation specialties (MOS)? The most common MOS is the infantry. Infantrymen, a.k.a. "grunts," are the packhorses and ground warriors of the military. These men are the "enlisted scum," the "hoi polloi," the workingmen soldiers—the grunts.

> The perverse eloquence at the bottom
> > Of humanity's heap
> Says things like…
> "If you ain't a Grunt, you ain't Shit."
>
> What a thing to call somebody—
> Pack-animal sweat and cannon fodder.

Anyone who can be that
    And still say that
Is as free as he's ever going to get.[11]

J. C. Muir

They had numerous duties. Some carried the M60 machine gun, others the radio (PRIC10), others the grenade launcher. Others were snipers in small, four to five man teams: Marines were two man teams. Others were mortarmen, carrying mortar rounds and the mortar itself. And others were forward observers for the artillery.

Much of their time was spent in mind-numbing boredom, punctuated by moments of sheer terror. They burned shit, they played cards, they got drunk when they could, and they smoked weed or did other, more overwhelming, drugs such as heroin. Then they were taken out to the field and dropped off.

Being dropped into action. Generally, a helicopter took them out. Frequently, they were dropped into a firefight (a "hot LZ," meaning that the landing zone was in the middle of active armed conflict). Many times they were literally dropped, as the helicopter could not land because of the intensity of the enemy fire. In that case, soldiers had to jump with a full pack from a distance of six to ten feet into the sharp blades of elephant grass, where there might be rocks and other hazards.

Once on the ground, soldiers had to sort things out very quickly, with rounds flying everywhere. Most of the time, the enemy was never seen. There were muzzle flashes from tree lines, or just bullets whizzing

---

11 Muir, J. Cruickshank. *Tigers and Songbirds*, (the Muir Studio, 2007).

by, with no observable enemy in sight. After going through this intensely fearful activity, soldiers picked up their wounded, checked the enemy dead for papers, and did a body count.

One of the many frustrations Vietnam veterans struggled with as soldiers was gaining territory, only to leave it for enemy reoccupation. The soldiers would capture a hill and hold it against fierce attacks from the NVA. However, once the attacks stopped, the company of soldiers would move out, allowing the return of the NVA. Veterans tell me accounts of taking territory, leaving it, and returning, only to have to fight for it again.

The body count kept and maintained by officers was widely reviled by the grunts for its obvious exaggeration and its minimization of the sacrifice on both sides. The way they saw it, lives had been reduced to a score being kept by Pentagon politicians and REMFs (rear echelon motherfuckers). Apparently, much of the score was a lie manufactured to maintain the mythology of the war. As one veteran said, "We killed the entire population of Vietnam several times."

After regathering in the LZ, the soldiers would begin a patrol, searching for more enemy contact. Both the Viet Cong and the NVA would choose when they would make contact. It was rare that the American soldiers would be able to catch the NVA by surprise.

Steve was a lieutenant with Special Forces, assigned as an advisor to a squad of ARVNs. He led the ARVNs on patrols and frequently encountered the enemy. But the enemy was clever and resourceful, hitting and killing a few soldiers, then disappearing. The lieutenant saw that the enemy was becoming very effective at causing casualties and creating low morale amongst the ARVNs. "We had to interrupt their learning curve," he told me. "We had to kill a few of them."

The ARVNs and the lieutenant were on a patrol when enemy fire pinned them down. Steve was exultant! At last the enemy was stationary and fighting. "We had them right where we wanted them," he told me later, in treatment, smiling broadly at the apparent nonsense of his statement. He and the ARVN squad were pinned down by fire coming from a tree line. The lieutenant crawled to a small hill and radioed for air support. Soon, there were F-4 fighter jets strafing the tree line. Steve sent word down the ARVN line that they were going to charge the tree line. His only weapon was his .45 caliber pistol.

After the final run by the jets, he got to his feet and charged the tree line, firing as he went. He had no idea if the ARVNs were going to follow him or run in the other direction. Surprisingly, he was not receiving any fire from around the trees. Gaining the tree line, he was amazed to see that the VC had apparently completely disappeared. He was also surprised to see that all of the ARVNs had followed his charge.

Then they started to receive more fire from another tree line where the VC had retreated. Once again the jets strafed, and once again the lieutenant and the ARVNs charged. This time when the VC retreated, they were caught in the open, where the jets killed them.

That evening, the lieutenant retired to the officer's club. He was sitting at the bar when a colonel entered, went over to the lieutenant, and said, "Lieutenant, I understand that you had some contact out there."

"Yes sir," replied the lieutenant.

"Well, Lieutenant, if you ever do anything that stupid again, I'll shoot you myself."

Daily patrols were a major part of grunts' lives. The patrols kept the VC on edge and made it difficult for Charlie to set up booby traps and ambushes. But patrols were extremely stressful for soldiers. Someone had to walk point—to be the lead man down the trail. This was a soldier everyone relied on, a soldier who was able to detect booby traps and ambushes. However, the point man's life was not expected to be of great length.

A veteran told me that he had walked point the majority of his tour in Vietnam. He said that he was able to do it by simply telling himself, "I am a dead man." Every day he would get up and repeat this mantra of death. Yet he survived and came home. Though he no longer told himself that he was dead, he continued to have that attitude. He worked at many jobs, traveling across the country with his dog. Sometimes, for no apparent reason, he would drop his tools and leave without receiving pay or even notifying anyone of his departure. He was without friends, living in his truck. He came into the Vet Center in a state of deep depression, overwhelmed by hopelessness. After two years of individual treatment, he was ready for group work. Groups are more intense, and veterans need to be able to cope effectively through with individual treatment, prior to group work. In the group, suddenly one night he experienced an "AHA!" He realized that he was not dead but had continued to *think* of himself as dead. This insight began his work bringing himself home.

The soldiers encountered villages on their daily patrols. Sometimes the villages opened fire on the soldiers. The soldiers frequently responded by killing everyone in the village, including women and children.

Veterans are haunted by these actions. In treatment, it is important that the veterans' grief and sadness be encouraged and given room to honor the deaths of these civilians. However, it is also important to keep in mind that these actions occurred in the time of war, and that everything is different in the time of war. Some things are not excusable, regardless of the time; but still, they may be forgiven.

Forgiveness. The concept of forgiveness needs to be discussed with veterans in treatment. What does forgiveness mean to the veteran? What does it mean to you? Can you forgive the veterans you work with?

Some veterans need to ask for forgiveness daily. Similar to the Catholic "Hail Mary," the veteran can ask God to forgive him. The therapist should be careful not to underestimate the power of this request for forgiveness.

Banana Leaf Supper

It was hot, she was hot

It was dry, she was dry
She seemed brittle as parchment
Ready to flake to dust and blow away

Once it had been a nice house
Now it didn't stand out
Just another thatched roof bamboo hut
Standing out can be dangerous
The concrete pad of the old house
Remained to feed her memories
As she stirred a cauldron of rice
Her eyes slit to hide, she watched us

We slipped out of the trees
Quiet as the ghosts that
Haunted her village
She stirred and watched

I looked around and looked again
I tried to see, really see
I saw the rice, too much rice
She watched and stirred

It was hot, I was hot
It was dry, I was dry
She was cooking too much rice
She was feeding the VC at night

Vietnamese woman, ancient
Faces American boy, nineteen
And the chasm yawned before us
Then disappeared with a look

I decided not to take her prisoner
Not to burn her house, instead
I pulled down a banana leaf and held it out

For her to feed me some of the VC rice

The rest lined up and took some too
We sat, watchful, and ate the VC rice
Then we slipped back into the trees
Quiet as the ghosts that haunted her village.[12]

J. Cruickshank Muir

Ambushes. Besides patrols, soldiers set up ambushes. A small group would go out at night and set up alongside a trail. They waited for the VC or anyone out at this hour. Most nights were simply high anxiety/boredom. There were also the nights where the ambush would happen, when they would kill a group of VC. Some of those VC would be teenagers, women, and ordinary farmers who had been brutally coerced into helping carry ammunition.

After the ambush, the soldiers would check the dead bodies for papers and anything that might prove valuable to military intelligence. In doing that, the soldiers had to become personal with the dead enemy. When they looked at the VC's pouch, they frequently found pictures of wives, children, and parents. The soldiers began to realize that the enemy was human and not much different from them.

Wars are complicated, chaotic. Killing is not just of combatants but of anyone who is caught in the wrong place.

Helicopters. Another MOS that is frequent among veterans is the helicopter door gunner/crew chief. This is a unique specialty, with its own terms and difficulties.

---

12 Ibid.

The helicopters were of various kinds from the huge Chinooks (shit hooks), to the Huey gun ships, to the small Loges that provided reconnaissance information. Mostly, door gunner veterans have served on the Hueys and have become almost legendary among veteran culture.

While the helicopters brought the infantry into battle, it also got them out and saved the wounded. The sound of a helicopter is what triggers most veterans' intrusive thoughts. They can hear (and really feel) the helicopter, long before civilians have any awareness of its approach. The sound wakes them up at night and flashes them back to horrendous scenes filled with adrenalin and blood.

Door gunners had to stand in the doorway of the gun ship, firing an M60 machine gun from a variety of positions. Sometimes the gunner preferred to use a stand that the gun pivoted on, and sometimes the gunner devised a sling that the gun could be manipulated on.

Gunners have told me of seeing ground fire coming up at them as they descended. The ground fire looked like small balls bouncing in the air, which got steadily larger. Suddenly the balls would be as big as basketballs; and just as suddenly would have gone by the gun ship.

As the gun ship made its descent with the gunners (there were usually two, one for each side) firing the "sixties," the pilot would fire the rockets from just below the gunner's foot. Rock-and-roll music might be playing in the headphones, giving a surreal quality to this killing machine. When gunners in treatment talk about "going into a hot LZ," they become very agitated with overwhelming adrenaline. These memories increase the severity of their symptoms, unless the veteran has been adequately prepared (learned better coping responses).

The warrant officer/helicopter pilot is also a common patient in treatment. Army pilots, in particular, are renowned for their courage to fly into intense enemy fire to rescue trapped soldiers.

Of course helicopters were also shot down, and recalling these memories is vital for helicopter veterans. Door gunners frequently could see the enemy, unlike the lack of visual contact by infantry. Actually seeing someone get shot increases the severity of PTSD. Usually, in treatment, veterans express satisfaction over having killed the enemy; the enemy is, after all, trying to kill them. But they still struggle with the underlying belief that they themselves have sinned, and are now beyond redemption.

As with other MOS, being able to access the sensory memories of the door gunners and pilots are essential for their treatment.

The "brown water navy" or the Riverine Force was composed not only of the well-known swift boats, but also of other types of watercraft. There were larger boats, similar to the type in the movie *The African Queen*, and other extremely fast boats with little armor. The firepower of these latter boats was significant, but they lacked armored protection. They patrolled the rivers and attempted to intercept shipments of supplies for the NVA amongst the many Vietnamese fishing boats. Every confrontation was filled with possibilities of sudden death, and many times produced just that consequence.

The Marine recon force was stationed on a ship just off the coast of Vietnam and flown, by helicopter, to areas dominated by the NVA. The Marines would conduct sweeps of valleys, attempting to clear out the NVA. They would frequently have to fight for days, suffering many casualties. Then they would be flown back to the ship, where they would wait a few days and fly back into another valley. These Marines had almost daily firefights and major battles against very well-trained and well-armed forces.

The NVA were different from the VC. The VC were not just guerrilla fighters. They were also farmers or shopkeepers, during the day, and an insurgent force during the night. They were the peasant army that left wing politics rhapsodize. As tough and fearless as was the VC, the NVA were better trained and better equipped. The NVA commanders were extremely capable and shrewd, using their superior forces against America's superior firepower.

John was a Marine with the force recon. He had done endless sweeps with his company, chasing the NVA for days until the enemy either vanished or were killed. This time, his company was suddenly trapped by a battalion of NVA; a massive force of the enemy against a relatively small force of Marines.

Air support in the form of jets arrived quickly, but the jets picked the wrong target. Almost the entire company of Marines was killed before the jets realized their mistake. Only nine Marines out of one hundred-fifty were left.

They ran to the river, hearing the NVA behind them. They ran through the vines, with hooks that grabbed and held them for a terrifying moment, while they could hear the NVA behind them.

Finally, the nine Marines gained the river. They quietly slipped into the muddy, swiftly moving water, and crept along the banks, searching for the hollow breathing-reeds. As the NVA came to the river, the nine Marines were under the water, motionless, breathing quietly through their reeds. The NVA raked the banks of the river with their AKs. Rounds went spiraling by the submerged Marines.

Finally, the NVA left to search elsewhere. The Marines stayed in the river for three days. Now covered in leeches and sores, they ventured ashore to make radio contact. They were told to move to a clearing about two hundred meters away. They moved out. But they were noisy. The NVA heard them and once again gave chase.

The Marines entered the clearing, running, as hard as they could, and they saw at one end, about one hundred yards away, tanks, armored personnel carriers (APCs), artillery, about five hundred Marines, and gun ships. When they got about halfway to the American forces, the tanks opened up. The Marines could see the shells going over their heads and exploding behind them. Behind them were hundreds of NVA pouring out of the jungle into the clearing.

The Marines gained the security of the tanks and the artillery. Then they turned and watched the devastation, as the tanks and artillery showered the NVA with lethal bombardment.

Suddenly there was a roar, and the jets came down directing napalm, rockets, and machine gun fire. But the NVA continued to come out of the jungle—until a commander whistled a stop and the enemy retreated to the tree line, gathering their dead and wounded.

We were such a rag tag
    Boys Town marching band
Scruffy lot of beardless wonders
But with a big difference—
    Those with the guns get to be boss
Poor pious VC teenager
His all the right answers indoctrination failed him
And he must have thought it was a bad dream
    As we dug him out of the bush
Wide eyed

One minute he was the enemy
    Hated, sought, feared
No longer
Now he was ours
    No more to hurt but to succor

We needed to bring him back
    Back to our security
Back to our safety
Back to what even then we knew
    No other word for other than
    Home

Our holes
    Our sandbags

Bind him. Blindfold him, gag him
    He must not know the way we take him

Nor escape from us
Nor call out to his friends

Around us a sea of uncertainty
    A nation of uncertainty
A world of uncertainty
But here at last is something for which there can
    Be no question

Something to bind us to this other
    Scruffy know nothing kid
From so far away it hadn't even qualified for
    The third world yet
For he is ours
    No more the enemy
Now he is changed forever
Now he is our charge
Safe at last
    We are told to turn
Him over to the Army of the Republic for which we
stood
And without so much as a word
    An officer shoots him dead
No Wagnerian death dramatics
    He dropped like
a sack of wet shit
and the life was gone
    in less than a blink
no longer was he ours
    not to harm
no longer was he ours to bring back
they simply took him
    and they shot him
perhaps this small hemmingwayesque example

of Asian thinking was only
    to show the burly
Americans what bad really was
      Or perhaps he'd had a fight with his wife
        Or knew something we didn't
War harms more than the body
    It saps the spirit
Not only of people but of peoples
And this people had been
    At war for 400 years.[13]

J.C. Muir

When soldiers became "short timers"—when they had only thirty days left in their tour—then their anxieties would increase. A great fear would begin that having survived this long meant that they would be killed just before going home. They kept a "short-timer's stick," where the days left would be marked and then broken off.

Michael was a Marine in Vietnam. On his final day of duty, he got a ride to the airport from another Marine. The driver began suddenly began to drive the jeep onto the shoulder of the road. The shoulders were frequently covered with booby traps, and Michael became angry. He yelled at the other Marine to stop it, but the man just laughed. Then Michael pulled out his .45 and put the barrel against the other man's head. The driver looked at him and then laughed, "You're not going to do shit." And continued to swerve onto the shoulder. Michael made it to the airport safely.

I asked Michael, "What was that like to remember that?"

---

13 Ibid.

He replied, "That's just how it was. I know that, here, that doesn't make any sense. But it made perfect sense, there."

I persisted, "What were you aware of while you were remembering?"

"I felt angry," he answered. "But I feel angry about everything. I understand what that guy was doing. You had to do shit like that in order to keep your sanity."

Soldiers spent much of this time just before leaving was spent by soldiers in fantasies, avoiding the reality of the war. Escaping into fantasies of home, women, and friends was a powerful coping method for the intense trauma and stress of the war.

Most veterans continue to use the coping method of fantasy today to escape the stress of work, relationships, and responsibilities. Unfortunately, their escape through fantasy reduces their ability to perceive reality accurately. The more stressful veterans' lives are, the more they use fantasy to cope. The more they escape into fantasy, the less able they are to accurately discern reality. The less able they are to discern reality, the more stressful their lives become. And so on.

After the 1968 Tet offensive by the NVA, the morale of the soldiers deteriorated. It seemed clear that the war was not going to be won. Troops began to just go through the motions. Patrols would go only a few meters outside the wire/perimeter of the base camp and camp out for the night. Their purpose was to set up an ambush, but the risks were no longer acceptable.

Soldiers still engaged the enemy, did patrols, fought battles, and died—and all this in a war that had all but been abandoned by the American administration.

Welcome Home. "What a bunch of shit!" (discharge). Most soldiers DEROS'd from Vietnam. Sometimes they would still be in a firefight in a rice paddy when the helicopter came. The crew chief would call the soldier's name and add, "Come on, you're going home!" And then, as early as just two days later, the soldier would be on the streets of Oakland, California, with no debriefing, no counseling, and no welcome except for the hostility and anger of the war protesters.

In treatment, therefore—at this particular phase of treatment—it is important to stand up, shake the veteran's hand, and say, "Welcome home." The profound effect this has on veterans cannot be overstated. Finally, they get the respect—even belatedly—that they had wanted on their return from the war.

Upon returning, however, home turns out to be quite different from their fantasies. Instead of being greeted by a welcoming, grateful civilian population, soldiers coming home from Vietnam encountered an angry, hateful, and rejecting populace. Returning Marines would frequently be let off outside their base, where a mass of protesters would be yelling and throwing things at them.

One Marine told me, "We got to the gates, and the bus driver wouldn't go any further. There were protesters everywhere. We were all stunned. We had heard some stories but never imagined that our own country would have turned against us. You know, it wasn't like we had started this war, or even that we wanted to go fight. It was our job, our duty. Anyway, Gunny stands up and looks at the crowd. He shakes his head and says, 'What a bunch of shit! But this is what we're fighting for. Let's go!' We had to push our way through the crowd. I think I stepped on a couple of sandals with my boots along the way."

Even the military rejected the Vietnam veterans. Many veterans still had time on their active duty. These veterans were often put in front of the company during the morning roll call as an example of a "loser."

Stateside military (the military in the U.S. as opposed to the military in Vietnam) was very different from how it functioned in the war zone. Here, the military was once again concerned with haircuts, cleanliness, lines of authority, and other military essentials.

Vietnam veterans had grown used to the necessary aspects of the war, such as vigilance, readiness, and a willingness to die, but no longer considered the other military needs to be of much importance. The Vietnam veteran with a Combat Infantryman's Badge was a very different person from the stateside lieutenant in charge. The veteran generally had little or no respect for the lieutenant's authority. As a result, many veterans were given dishonorable discharges, discharges under honorable conditions, and general discharges—all of which prevented them from receiving benefits from the Veterans Administration. Going AWOL became almost an epidemic among the returnees in the early 1970s. Eventually, the military recognized the problem and began allowing Vietnam veterans "early outs."

However, the damage had been done, and Vietnam veterans had acquired a reputation as dangerous, violent, and emotionally unstable. When I began seeing veterans in my private practice in the early 1980s, the patient population soon increased and I needed a bigger, more accessible office. I contacted some local psychologists to request sharing their office. I met with a lot of positive and welcoming responses. Eventually, however, the psychologist would ask the key question: "What kind of a patient population do you see?"

"Mostly Vietnam veterans," I would answer.

There would be a pause, then a hedging statement: "I need to check with my landlord/partner/wife. I'll have to get back to you."

Being discharged from the military brought a new set of problems. Most veterans remember this time with ambivalence. They remember their relief at finally being free from the military structure—and their fear at now being on their own.

After Joe was discharged, he revealed to me in treatment, "There was an emptiness. It lasted about two or three months. I didn't know what to do. The military had run my life for so long, I really didn't have a clue about how to live."

Many veterans took their uniforms and, literally, put them in the trash. Some veterans refused to admit that they had been in the military, and didn't talk about it. If the subject of the war came up, they remained silent or changed the topic.

After I had been working at the Vet Center for a couple of years, I realized the enormous amount of energy it took for these veterans to maintain this silent cover. They had endured extreme trauma, in some cases, but never spoke of it.

One time I was at a party, talking to a woman and her husband. In the course of the conversation, my occupation as a veteran's therapist came up. The husband looked at me with some interest and said, "I was in Special Forces in Vietnam. I served two tours." His wife of five years looked at him in shock and said, "I didn't know you were in the military."

These silent veterans, the ones who tried not to be noticed for their military service, also tried to move on with their lives. Their success varied. Some had more than numerous jobs. Some had more than numerous marriages and children. Some had countless years of substance abuse. Some veterans went to prison. Others spent time in jail, or simply had brutal encounters with whomever they could. Some veterans would go to bars and pick a fight with the biggest or meanest person. It didn't matter to the veteran if he got beat up, or vice versa; afterwards, his physical pain would take his attention away from his emotional and mental anguish.

But there were also veterans who got married, stayed married, got a job, kept the job, had kids, raised the kids, and by all accounts were productive citizens. Yet these veterans maintained a façade and refused to discuss their nightmares, depression, anxiety, withdrawal, and angry rages. They began to assume that their difficulties were "normal."

Both these groups come to therapy. The therapist is their last hope.

As Vietnam veterans continue to age, they will seek treatment in greater numbers.

Groups

After veterans have been through individual treatment and appear capable of coping effectively with their memories, it is time for them to be in a group. Individual treatment must precede group treatment for several reasons.

1. Group treatment is more intense, as the memories and experiences of other veterans bring up their own apparently forgotten memories, whether neglected or not adequately dealt with in individual treatment.

2. Individual treatment prepares veterans for the intensity of the group, and prevents them from being flooded with overwhelming emotions and experiencing severe emotional pain.

Group Logistics. In terms of group size, I prefer to run small groups (five to seven veterans). In terms of their population, I have run both homogeneous groups (a particular war) and heterogeneous groups (with veterans from more than one war), and have found both to be very effective. In terms of group duration, I strongly urge long-term groups (two to five years).

The group process is much more complicated than individual treatment, and has many different levels of dynamics. Therefore, I recommend that a therapist never try to do more than one group in a day. If the treatment facility where the therapist is working requires more than one group per day, I would state that this requirement is verging on malpractice, as it violates a standard of care.

Group treatment of veterans is so complicated that it could easily fill a whole other book! It can be exhausting for the therapist to keep track of each veteran's different levels of awareness, to pay attention to each veteran's emotional states, to stay present in the session (ninety to one hundred-twenty minutes), and to bring insight to bear on the traumas.

Groups are also a bonding for veterans, enabling a reemergence of camaraderie, a sharing of experiences, a renewal of emotions, an awakening of compassion for others, and an opportunity for heartfelt expressions. Veterans tend to linger outside the therapy office long after the group has ended, not wanting to leave and again be strangers in their world.

Group Treatment Process. Although the process of group treatment is similar to individual treatment, it is extremely important to always find out how each veteran is processing the group. Meditation and other spiritual practices are a great help in groups.

I begin by asking veterans to present their current issues, and I work with their present issues for a period of time. Then one veteran (the "focus" veteran) will discuss a particular stage of his or her life, generally in the military, and will be encouraged to share whatever emotions come up during that process.

After the focus veteran has reached some point in his or her process, and the session has about twenty minutes left, I ask each of the other veterans what the presentation was like for them. I encourage all the veterans to share their emotions as they relate to what was presented. However, many times this is very difficult for veterans, as they are overwhelmed by memories. What has been brought up by the focus veteran may have stimulated such intense memories in other veterans that they need to continue to process those memories instead of being required to share/ express their emotions.

Groups are a powerful way of helping veterans move into society. Rather than simply adjusting, however, now they have improved insight, effective communication skills, and an awareness that goes beyond the ordinary.

The third practice of concentration helps to establish that greater awareness.

Concentration III:
A Practice of Sending Light through the Eyes.

Therapists should use their clinical judgment in using this practice. Veterans' emotional states need to be balanced, with symptoms that are only mild to moderate. Generally, this practice is introduced to groups that have been meeting regularly for at least two years.

This practice is also based on veterans already having learned to hold in their minds an image of an object, and to create in their minds an image of a circle of light. This practice begins the awareness of how to send light from their eyes. As a result of the increased awareness of light, feelings of compassion and kindness also increase, with a concomitant reduction of anger.

To begin, ask the veterans to do the following:

* Close their eyes.

* Inhale.

* Turn their eyes up (looking at the spot just above and between their eyes).

* Gently put the bottom of their tongue against the roof of their mouth (the soft palate), and

* Gently hold their breath. (Let them know that this is not a contest to see who can hold their breath the longest).

* While they are holding their breath, ask them to become aware (at first, just creating the image) of a light descending through the top of their head (the crown).

* When they exhale, have them bring their eyes and their tongue down, sending the light out through their still-closed eyes.

This exercise has a powerful impact on compassion, self-confidence, and the discovery of the more refined nafs.

Chapter Two
Iraq/Afghanistan

After having the power of life and death...

Why Iraq War Veterans Want to Return to War

Every Iraq veteran who has come for treatment with me wants to return to Iraq.

Why? At first, it seems very odd that veteran soldiers would want to return to a place of danger and stress.

And yet there are several reasons for this. The most commonly given one is that the job has been left undone and comrades have been left behind. However, another, perhaps more important, reason is veterans' need for meaning.

The Need for Meaning. In the brilliant book, *War is a Force That Gives Us Meaning*,[1] Chris Hedges focuses on the meaningfulness that takes place in war. Most civilians think of war as a horrible, nightmarish experience. However, the meaning available in ordinary life tends to pale next to the meaning of being one of several thousand men and women who are heavily armed with immense firepower in a foreign

---

1 Hedges, Chris. *War is a Force that Gives Us Meaning* (New York: Random House, 2003).

country, with the task of subduing a resilient and resourceful enemy.

After having the power of life and death, experiencing extreme terror, demonstrating great bravery, and having the benefit of deep camaraderie, the civilian aftermath of stocking shelves in grocery stores (a job that many Iraq veterans are given as civilians) loses whatever small amount of meaning it might initially have had.

Intimacy and Trust: Regular Ego Development in Adolescence and Its Disruption

Veterans of the Iraq/Afghanistan wars are usually much younger, at a different level of emotional development, and have a more recent experience of the trauma of war than do other veterans, even veterans of the Persian Gulf War.

Because they were deployed to a war zone while young (and still are young after discharge), Iraq veterans miss out on the kind of civilian social interaction that helps them acquire the ability to share ideas about themselves with others.

If adolescence prepared the young men and women who become soldiers with a sense of identity, then these soldiers are ready to form intimate relationships. Critical experiences during this period that foster this ability include: learning when to lower personal boundaries; how to be vulnerable with another; and how to relate to someone in an intimate manner. If a sense of trust has been formed in infancy and early childhood, young men and women will think of themselves as unique, worthwhile, and able to share with another human being without losing that identity.

However, military training and war experiences tend to disrupt regular ego development. Therefore, in treatment, if the therapist initially focuses on ego development, that disruption by the military experience can be seen as a possibility of a new awareness—one that can move veterans beyond ordinary civilian perspectives. Perhaps the most common military awareness that helps in ego development is the sense of self-sacrifice. There is a willingness by soldiers to sacrifice themselves for another soldier. However, veterans are disappointed when they discover that civilians don't share the soldiers' commitment.

Because the closed culture of the military encourages self-disclosure only within the military, veterans feel that civilians do not understand military life and are not to be trusted with their experiences of the reality of military service. Instead of learning the value of self-disclosure and trusting others, veterans learn that self-disclosure is dangerous outside of one's own squad, and that trusting is only possible if there is a unanimous agreement regarding the mission (i.e., kill the enemy). As a result, both men and women veterans come out of the military guarded, threatened, anxious, and always alert for possible danger.

If the experience of gaining intimacy was not already part of veterans' development before becoming soldiers, it is likely that they will later become isolated in civilian society.

The Time Factor: Iraq War Trauma Is Still Fresh

The traumas of war are very recent for the Iraq/Afghanistan veterans. While their war is both different from and similar to Vietnam, the biggest difference is the recentness of time. For Afghanistan veterans, trauma could literally have happened as recently as a month ago or even a few weeks. These veterans' symptoms are raw, overwhelming, confusing, disorienting, troubling, and terrifying.

On the other hand, this time proximity can also work in veterans' favor. Their difficulties are not chronic; their attitudes are not well-established over decades, as is the case with veterans of earlier wars. Their issues are current, and these veterans still have clear memories of how they used to think and perceive the world before going off to war. However, veterans do not necessarily want to return to this prewar innocence. Mostly, they want the anxiety, nightmares, and furious anger to subside.

What is a greater challenge with younger veterans is establishing rapport, due to the disruption of regular ego development. Women therapists often have greater success, as Iraq veterans do not have the same feelings about women as returning Vietnam veterans did. Iraq/Afghanistan veterans still expect that women will be nurturing, not accusing and rejecting. In addition in Iraq, women served alongside men in combat. Most male Iraq veterans report that women soldiers proved just as competent and brave as their male counterparts.

The Backdoor Draft

The current army is reportedly a volunteer army— "reportedly," because many of the soldiers have been prevented from being discharged. This is sometimes termed the "backdoor draft," indicating an enforced extension of military service. In addition there have been several activations of the "ready reserve," a group of veterans who already have completed their obligations for active duty but are placed on the ready reserve list for a certain number of years. During that time, veterans may be reactivated into active duty. Some Iraq veterans have reportedly served up to five tours in Iraq.

The wars in Iraq and Afghanistan developed into a war against an unknown enemy. After the collapse of the Iraqi army, Iraqi soldiers were disarmed and sent home. This turned out to be a critical mistake, as those Iraqi soldiers had no way of supporting themselves and their families. Their anger and frustration made them willing volunteers in various insurgent groups. Afghanistan is a country made up largely of different relatively isolated tribes. This means that the U.S. soldiers are not fighting against a well-armed, well-trained enemy, such as the North Vietnamese Army (NVA) but are confronted with a guerrilla foe more like the Viet Cong. American soldiers in Iraq and Afghanistan fight/fought against a civilian enemy made up of diverse and sometimes disparate individuals.

Both the Viet Cong, Iraqi insurgents, and the Afghani tribesmen are similar in that each was unrecognizable as an enemy until they performed a hostile action. In Vietnam, Iraq, and Afghanistan any civilian could be the enemy. In aiming to kill American soldiers, VC, Iraqi insurgents, and Afghani mujahidin make extensive use of women and children. Both these enemy groups reportedly disregard the safety of their own civilians in their attempts to kill American personnel. As in Vietnam, in Iraq and Afghanistan this sort of "no safe place" gives rise to the killing of civilians by American soldiers, a sort of "shoot first and let God sort it out" attitude.

The Effects of More Powerful Technology. This mindset (ready to kill) is certainly understandable when any car can contain enough explosive to kill many soldiers and when even U.S. trained Afghani soldiers are capable of killing Americans. Witnessing apparently innocent civilians suddenly turn and toss grenades into a squad can create an extreme readiness on the part of the soldiers to fire on them.

However, one difference between Vietnam and Iraq is the use of new technology by the U.S. While night-vision goggles ("starlight scope") were used somewhat in Vietnam, their increased use in Iraq greatly intensified the effectiveness of the troops, and made the night just as dangerous as the day for the enemy.

The Bradley fighting machine exemplifies the awesome firepower that the U.S. is able to deploy. Heavily armored, the Bradley has a 25-millimeter cannon, with depleted uranium shells that are powerful enough to pierce armor. In addition, it has a gas-powered machine gun that is reputed to put out almost twice as many rounds per minute as did the previous M60 machine gun. Finally, it carries at least six troops bearing several automatic weapons.

However, the cannon alone is such a powerful weapon that if one round were to hit a person, there would be little left of that person to identify. Furthermore, the depleted uranium shell casings are now reported to be responsible for several different types of cancer—not only in the civilian population, but also affecting the soldiers involved in the use and loading of the cannon.

Other important aspects of technology in Iraq are the Internet and access to television. Soldiers make liberal use of email, Internet video calls, websites with the latest videos of bombings, Facebook, and pornography. Many U. S. soldiers become so absorbed in Internet sites that they continue viewing military actions even after being discharged. The veterans watch endless videos of IED (improvised explosive devices) explosions, killings of insurgents, and insurgent posted attacks.

The Effect of an Urban War. The Iraq War was primarily an urban war, as opposed to the jungles and rice paddies of Vietnam, and the mountains and hills of Afghanistan. Although there was initially some desert fighting, that was quickly overwhelmed by the United States' use of jets, armored tanks, Bradleys, and infantry.

When the American soldiers left Kuwait and headed across the desert to Iraq, the endless nothingness of the desert began to attack the soldiers' psyches, which were used to quickly changing screens of commercials and video games. To replicate this kind of external stimulation, Allan pasted large pictures of nude women in provocative poses inside the tanks. He would masturbate while driving through the desert's brown emptiness. Other soldiers would play music, attempting to distract themselves from what they experienced as interminable silence.

The convoy was part of the early invasion. The majority of the invading force had already pushed through the highway, leaving behind the remnants of the Iraq Army. The Iraqi soldiers quickly discarded their uniforms but not their weapons. This made them indistinguishable from civilians.

When the first town of any size suddenly materialized, the convoy slowed down as crowds of people surged onto the street. The convoy commander ordered the troops to keep moving. There were about six to eight miles still to negotiate before they would be through the town.

Jim was riding in a Humvee in the front of the column. Then an Iraqi man stepped out from the crowd with an apparatus on his shoulder, which Jim recognized as a rocket-propelled grenade (RPG) launcher. He shouted to the driver, who immediately steered the Humvee off to the side of the road.

The man fired the RPG; but because it was poorly aimed, it went over the soldiers' heads. The convoy came to a stop and was immediately surrounded by the crowd. The commander yelled at the soldiers, "Keep driving, don't stop!" Then they began to receive fire from the roofs of the buildings. The Bradleys returned the fire, which allowed the convoy to begin moving. But the civilians blocked the way and wouldn't move.

The commander gave the order to shoot anyone in the way. American machine guns opened up on the crowd, quickly killing many civilians and causing a complete panic, as everyone ran for cover. Then the soldiers again began to receive fire from the roofs, as well as from assorted doorways.

The commander gave the command for the scouts to dismount and begin the work of clearing the streets. The infantry, including Jim, began to fight their way along the streets, quickly killing the enemy that stayed to fight. Most of the fire from the roofs ceased.

The commander ordered the infantry to secure (clear out any hostiles) the houses along the street. These infantry, such as Jim, were young soldiers, untrained in kicking down doors and clearing houses. But they set about their work methodically, going to houses, knocking, then kicking down doors, and killing whoever opposed them. It took two days of steady fighting before the convoy was able to completely move through the town.

Treatment

Therapeutic treatment with Iraq veterans is both similar to and different from treatment of veterans of other wars.

Jim was one of the soldiers who had been part of that convoy, as well as being involved in many other extremely tragic incidents. He had been back from Iraq for two years when his roommates insisted that he get help. That's when he came to me for treatment.

"They tell me I scream and yell at night," he remarked.

"What's it like to hear that?" I asked.

"It's embarrassing. I know it's true, I wake myself up all the time."

As a result of the pain and death he had witnessed in Iraq, Jim had decided to enter the medical profession. But his anger consistently got the better of him; and one drunken evening, he came very close to being arrested for assault.

Jim poured himself into treatment. With the details of his time in Iraq still current in his mind, he was able to relive those days with great intensity. The number of tragic experiences he survived was monumental.

I remarked, "I'm very impressed that you are able to function at all."

"It doesn't seem like I'm functioning so good," he said.

"Maybe if you realized that you know a lot more than anyone else, you might appreciate yourself," I suggested.

He looked surprised. "I should be more positive?"

"No, that's not it. How do you want to be?"

Johnny looked at the floor. "Doc, I just want to be OK. I am tired of being angry and not sleeping."

"Look, you have had experiences that are completely different. I don't know of anyone who has survived what you have. Give yourself a break. Look at yourself and say, 'Wow, I did it. What I have done is almost unheard of.'" I watched him carefully.

"So I should feel good about destroying a house with women and children?" he asked.

I felt frustrated, and waited until my frustration subsided. Then I explained, "We talked about why that happened. It's *good* that you feel bad. I mean, if you didn't feel bad about that, I would be afraid of you. You were in a war. You did your job. Your job was to kill the enemy. You did that job very well with honor and bravery. Stop beating the shit out of yourself." I waited as he processed.

Smiling, now, he said, "Yeah, OK. I get it. If I stop whining and just get on with it, then I'll be OK."

I felt even more frustrated. "You think that will do it? You have a responsibility for a lot of lives, and you are trying to honor that responsibility. That is really incredible. Instead of trying to bury your memories, you are bringing them out, facing yourself every day, and trying to be honest. But if you are really going to be honest, then you can't just look at your negative stuff. You also have to accept your positive stuff. Being honest means *appreciating yourself*, as well as tormenting yourself with difficult memories."

Jim looked slightly relieved. "Thanks," he said. "I kinda felt that, but I wasn't sure. I mean, if I told this shit to anyone else, they would probably hate me and not want to ever talk to me again."

I thought for a minute, then said, "You might be surprised. But yeah, most people don't want to hear this. They want to continue to think of war as it's portrayed in movies and books. They don't want to hear about it from someone who was there. So you've got a real mission—to teach us about reality, and, in the process, find yourself."

Establishing Rapport in Treatment

Establishing rapport with an Iraq/Afghanistan veteran is different from establishing rapport with older veterans.

Recognizing their stage of emotional development and their level of nafs allows therapists to intervene appropriately. Given a little practice, it is easy to determine a veteran's level of ego development and corresponding level of understanding. Listening carefully, paying attention to body posture, and helping veterans pace their expressions generally will allow for the development of rapport.

Childhood and adolescence were not that long ago for most Iraq/Afghanistan veterans. Therefore it is important to help them remember those times in detail. When therapists hold an atmosphere of no judgment, an open willingness to learn, and clear acceptance of the veterans, a therapeutic environment is established.

Determining Veterans' Level of Nafs. But for therapists, even more important than rapport in the treatment of Iraq veterans is the ability to determine their level of nafs.

Nafs are not necessarily tied to chronological age. A young person may have a more evolved level of nafs than an older individual. With practice involving prayer, intuition, and meditation, therapists can increase their sensitivity to their own nafs as well as to those of their patients.

Such intuition initially may be only a very faint awareness, a slight feeling that something is going on other than how it appears.

Frank had been coming in for several sessions, always presenting himself as an ordinary twenty-something interested in the same things as others in his age group. He said all the right things, had the right tone of voice, and held his body in an easy, relaxed manner. However, there had also been something odd about his presentation, as if it were an act. When I felt we had developed a sufficiently trusting relationship that I could offer some mild confrontation, I asked him,

"Are we talking about what is important to you? I mean, you don't seem like you are really all that interested in video games, texting, and football."

The young veteran looked slightly surprised, but then said, "I'm not. I'm just trying to fit in. Most guys I know have never left home. I've seen and done things they don't know anything about. But I want friends. I don't want to just hang out with veterans."

After that exchange, we were able to immeasurably increase the depth of treatment.

Therapists must be prepared to hear about exceptional cases of mistaken attacks on civilians from Iraq/Afghanistan veterans, even more than what was heard from Vietnam veterans. After all, there are no uniforms to distinguish insurgents from the rest of the civilian population. And even the ordinary civilian will quickly turn against the American soldier, given the proper opportunity.

The soldiers had driven four Humvees into a courtyard. The major was in one in the front. He dismounted and went into the main house to have a conference with one of the local chiefs. The rest of the soldiers stood in various places, watching the crowd, alert but relaxed. Various townspeople gathered to watch the soldiers. Some children approached the group, but were threatened by the soldiers and stepped back.

The major soon returned and stood for a moment talking with the chief. Suddenly one of the soldiers, John, noticed a hand, holding what looked like a rock, come over the wall. Someone shouted, "Grenade!"

and John dove for the cover of the Humvee. The explosion sent shrapnel everywhere, lacerating the legs of another soldier who had sought refuge in another Humvee.

When John recovered from the blast, he discovered that his rifle was missing. He searched frantically for it as the group began to take in rounds from small arms. He found it under the Humvee—just as the major, bleeding badly from a throat wound, yelled at the men to get in the vehicles and "Get moving!"

The townspeople blocked the narrow exit from the courtyard, and the major yelled to keep going. Men, women, and children were now throwing rocks and occasionally grenades at the troops, and others were firing from the rooftops. The soldiers returned fire, drove through the crowd, and sped back to the base, firing randomly as they went until the major ordered them to stop firing.

Spiritual Healing of Veterans' Wounds. Once, when I was on an individual spiritual retreat, spending days repeating sacred words, meditating on light, and offering prayer, I would often be confronted with images of suffering and violence. I tended to dismiss these images as just the detritus of watching television and movie entertainments, but still I was sufficiently disturbed to mention the images to my retreat guide. She said, "There is not an easy way for the mind to understand such things." And then she recommended, "If it is possible, go deeply into the heart of Christ." I tried; but of course, that is easier said than done. And to this day, I remain without a real understanding of such horror.

Veterans who already have a spiritual inclination generally dismiss the role of a deity in such warfare actions. They assert that humans perpetrate violence, and that God has little, if anything, to do with it.

Perhaps that is true. However, I also believe that nothing happens without God—that God made everything out of Himself.

Another explanation is that part of God is unconscious; that is, part of God does not know that He is God; and we are that part. Our manifestation as individuals is God's willingness to suffer so that all of His parts might know His perfection. That sounds right to me; but the truth is, of course, I really don't know for sure.

Regardless of why there is such violence against one another, our work as therapists is to help those individuals who have seen, received, and acted out violence.

Treatment Regarding the Nafs. A way of thinking about how to proceed with treatment is to first assume that our nafs are the basis of our awareness. The more developed our nafs, the greater our awareness. In the limited nafs, the more we think of only ourselves, the more we are concerned with just our own happiness, and the more we resist understanding other points of view, the more likely is the outcome of more wars.

In the limited nafs, the more we allow our inner war (the inner jihad) to be won by our lower self, the more we increase the probability that there will continue to be conflict and hostility. However, allowing the more developed nafs to determine our beliefs means loving even those who hurt us, caring about

those who create difficulty, and not allowing ourselves to be dragged into petty squabbles.

This is our purpose as therapists: first of all, to raise
our own levels of awareness; to increase the development of our nafs into a greater understanding; and
then help others to raise theirs.

Perhaps only a few will understand our intentions;
but this is not important. The ancient Sufis were hidden, unknown, and difficult to find as self-proclaimed
Sufis. However, those hidden Sufis were readily
available as friends: as someone who could be trusted, someone who cared. Certainly, our work can
have vital importance on the existence of millions
of people, regardless of their beliefs, levels of understanding, and narrow prejudices. If, as therapists, we
are able to reduce the willingness to use violence as a
solution, perhaps that will affect the level of violence
in the world.

Karl Marlantes, a Marine lieutenant in Vietnam,
the recipient of the Navy Cross, and the author of
Matterhorn[2] and *What it is Like to Go to War*,[3] in a
recent interview made the point that war is the result
of political failure. Policies made by politicians turn
out to create international/domestic difficulties and
armed conflict follows. Young men and women are
sent to wage violence in the name of government's
failure. As a result, violence as a solution is perpetu-
ated. If it is possible to reduce the willingness to solve

2 Marlantes, Karl. *Matterhorn: A Novel of the Vietnam War*
(New York: Atlantic Monthly Press, 2010).
3 Marlantes, Karl. *What It Is Like to Go to War.* (New York:
Atlantic Monthly Press, 2011).

failure by waging war through treatment of veterans, then our mission has earth-shaking possibilities.

In treatment, we follow the same process with Iraq and Afghanistan veterans as described in the previous chapter on treating Vietnam veterans. However, because Iraq/Afghanistan veterans are generally much younger than Vietnam veterans, the opportunity to interrupt their development of the disorder is much greater. Even regardless of the age difference, the traumatic incidents are considerably more recent. In Vietnam we are now looking at over at least thirty-three years—in some cases, even forty-four years—since the trauma of war occurred. Vietnam veterans may have adjusted to their symptoms as being normal. They believe that they were changed by the war but do not generally believe that they have any choice regarding how they continue to act and behave. In most cases, these older veterans believe that the past is stronger than the future.

Iraq and Afghanistan veterans are different in terms of distance from the traumatic incidents. Iraq veterans are still confused about their symptoms and why they are happening. They don't understand their anger, depression, anxiety, and nightmares. In addition, Iraq veterans still have hope that the future will allow them to put the traumas in the past. They hope that time will heal them and that their psychic wounds will subside as they adjust to civilian society.

Afghanistan veterans are still in the rawness of their anger. They struggle with controlling the anger but then become out of control and end up in jail. Or they are so frightened of what they might do

242

they commit suicide rather than being a danger to American society.

Many Afghanistan veterans had extensive interaction with civilians, and others were almost completely isolated. However, everyone felt, as in Vietnam and Iraq, that there was no "safe place." Karl Marlantes has pointed out that the lack of a safe place is one of the major differences between the current wars and WWII. In WWII there was a rear where there was a minimal chance of enemy attack but in Vietnam, Iraq, and Afghanistan there was/is nowhere immune to the enemy.

The Afghanistan veteran thus presents the same complicated group of symptoms as do the other veterans of current wars. Treatment of these veterans has to proceed with the understanding that veterans are individuals who have shared an experience unique to a particular group of veterans.

The terrain in Afghanistan is quite different from that of either Vietnam or Iraq. Instead of jungles or buildings there are mountains, rocky hills, and long open landscapes. The Afghanistan veteran may have spent long hours in isolation without the benefit of electronic reprieves from the possibility of snipers.

Boredom, punctuated by periods of intense violence, is the hallmark of all of the current wars. Sebastian Junger was imbedded with a group of Marines in Afghanistan, and in his book *War*,[4] he recounts the story of the Marine officer walking by, mumbling to himself, "God, I hope somebody shoots at us today."

The best time to effect treatment. The disorder is most susceptible to treatment in its acute phase.

4 Junger, Sebastian, *War* (New York: Twelve, 2011).

Major resistances. The major resistance to treatment from the Iraq veteran is the belief that the symptoms will disappear without treatment. Most Iraq veterans are not well-oriented to treatment, regardless of gender. While public knowledge of psychotherapy has progressed, it is still largely perceived as a strange process that either makes people worse or does nothing at all.

This resistance is also evident in Afghanistan veterans. However, that war has been going on long enough that a variety of Afghanistan veterans will enter treatment. They may have been discharged for several years or just a few months. They may have done six to eight tours of Afghanistan or just one to two. They may have seen actual fire fights or just stayed at the Forward Operating Base (FOB).

In addition, the stigma of going to a therapist continues to be a major block with most young veterans. The "suck it up" attitude is basic to all soldiers. However, Vietnam veterans have done a great deal to demystify treatment and to make it more acceptable to the younger Iraq veterans.

Iraq veterans in general have a great deal of respect for Vietnam veterans, but they still have the younger person's arrogance. Iraq veterans sometimes call the older veteran generation, "the old fools." But when I have included Iraq veterans along with a group of Vietnam veterans, the results have been very positive. Not only did Iraq veterans express admiration to Vietnam veterans, but later they also confided to me that they do not want to be that age (fifty to sixty) and "still that fucked up."

Afghanistan veterans come back to a public generally tired of the current war. The primary reason for the war, ostensibly to remove Afghanistan as a haven for al-Qaeda, has apparently ended.

Goal Setting. Because Iraq and Afghanistan veterans enter treatment unsure of its purpose, its method, and its applicability to their difficulties, veterans need to discuss their anxieties and fantasies regarding psychotherapy with their therapists before setting goals.

Once the process of treatment has been adequately clarified, the veteran can establish goals. Then the therapist can outline the treatment plan and how it will impact the veteran, both in terms of the initial increase of difficulties and the eventual decrease of symptom severity.

Childhood and adolescence are still fresh in the mind of Iraq/Afghanistan veterans, and the relationship with parents may still be a factor in their lives. Veterans may still be unaware of how to manage finances, and may already be in serious debt. They may be struggling with whether to go to work or go to school. They may be concerned about what being in treatment for PTSD will mean to their employment possibilities. If veterans are still on active duty, they will be appropriately concerned what treatment for PTSD will mean to a military career. (This varies, but generally it means the soldier will not "make rank"— that is, move up the military ladder.)

Wars always challenge our ideas about what is fair, what is ethical, and what is moral. We expect young people to make those moral decisions in split seconds—decisions that result in loss of life. The aftermath is generally one of torment and over-whelming confusion.

Louis, a young veteran, was recently married, still in the service, and struggling with his emotional regrets over a decision he had made in Iraq. He had been involved in a killing at a checkpoint. His sergeant gave an order not to shoot, but then the sergeant did just the opposite. Louis had to decide whether to report the sergeant or to maintain silence. He chose the latter, but now he still struggled with that decision.

"What would have happened if you had reported the sergeant?" I asked him.

The young man smiled and looked away. There was a silence as he decided how to respond. "That isn't the point," he said finally. Then he asked, "Do you understand duty?"

"I recognize how important it is to you to have followed through with what the military requires," I replied. "I'm not sure how I would have responded."

The young man looked at the floor and then looked around the room. "Easy to say," he finally stated.

"Right," I answered. "So do you want to work on easing your conscience about this, or is it important to keep fucking with yourself?"

Prescribing Coping Skills. Once rapport has been established with the veteran and the treatment plan has been described, then coping skills need to be prescribed and worked on until they have been improved.

Chronological Sequence of Exploration. At this point, the basic plan is to start with childhood. The sequence is essentially the same as for the more chronic type of PTSD, as found in the older veterans from WWII, Korean, and Vietnam; that is:

* childhood
* adolescence
* entry into the military
* basic training
* advanced training
* deployment, and
* return home.

Requirements on the Part of the Therapist. Therapists must be prepared for Iraq/Afghanistan veterans to be less patient with treatment (they don't understand how this is going to help), more threatened by the therapist's insights (defensive and argumentative), and less expressive with their thoughts (unable to articulate emotions other than anger and grief).

Therapeutic silence/interventions in the form of questions. A therapeutic silence is important to keep during the times when Iraq veterans experience a sense of being confronted. Therapeutic interpretations must be done carefully, and almost always in the form of a question; for example, "It sounds like you're angry with the sergeant?"

Let the veteran teach you. If there are arguments and unresolved disagreements, it means that the current form of treatment is not working. Veterans must not only feel safe in treatment; they also must feel understood. That usually means that the veterans get to teach the therapist about the war. A famous, possibly apocryphal, letter from an Iraq veteran and widow that is currently making the rounds on the Internet expresses a basic message for both pro- and anti-war advocates: "If you haven't been there, shut the fuck up!"

In addition, the specific nature of the veterans' MOS (military occupation specialty) gave them a different experience of the war than for other veterans. The tank driver had a different experience from the Bradley dismount, whose experience was different from the captain who investigated and compiled casualty lists, and so on. However, all these experiences are similar in that the camaraderie, the meaning, and the adrenalin of the war are touchstones in their lives. Again it also must be remembered that veterans are individuals and each will respond differently to similar experiences.

But most combat veterans question their actions and whether or not their actions were warranted, adequate, and appropriate. They had a job to do, and they did the job to the best of their abilities, regardless of how they feel about the official justification for the war.

Soldiers have always found humor in the most desperate of situations. In Iraq, soldiers discovered an interesting use for the heating element in the Meals Ready to Eat (MRE). If they took out the heating element, put it in a Gatorade bottle filled with water and small stones, shook up the bottle, and threw it at somebody, it would make a very satisfying explosion. In addition, the small stones would sting and scare other soldiers or small children.

Veterans all find that story very funny, and even comforting. GI humor maintains its basic adolescent status, regardless of the war.

Don't respond with horror/outrage when veterans finally share their secrets. As veterans begin to feel trusting enough to share their experiences in war, this will present their therapist with a dilemma. For example, a veteran may ask, "Should I have shot that _____ [enemy, lieutenant, child, woman, etc.]?" While to some degree it doesn't matter how the therapist responds, there are some responses that are unhelpful and even damaging. The worst response is one of horror and outrage, regardless of how well deserved it might be. The important thing is that veterans are finally expressing their experiences in therapy— secrets they have been struggling for months, or even years.

The Process of Forgiveness. Self-forgiveness often does not come easily to veterans. Asking a veteran, "How much longer do you need to suffer?" may begin the process of forgiveness.

What does it mean to forgive? *Understanding* is a significant part of forgiveness, and it also helps to open the heart. After that, reparation in some form helps to hasten the process.

There is *always* a way out of hell as the following Buddhist story illustrates.

There once was a horrible man. He murdered and tortured people and robbed them of all their possessions. Finally the people caught him and put him to death. He went to hell, where he became a demon. After thousands of years in hell, the demon became weary of the torture and mayhem. He prayed to Buddha to release him from hell.

The Blessed One heard his prayer and asked the demon if he had ever done anything for anyone. The

Blessed One could see all of the demon's past lives and saw that the demon had once not stepped on a spider. The demon had allowed the spider to live out of a small spark of compassion.

The Buddha sent a spider spinning a web into hell. The Blessed One told the demon to climb out of hell on the spider's web.

The demon was unsure about the web's strength. He pulled on it and it held, so he began to climb. As he climbed he began to feel a sense of exhilaration at the possibility of escaping from hell. He thought how clever he was at simply praying. Then the web began to shake. The demon looked down and saw that the other demons were also trying to escape from hell on the spider's web.

"Get off! It's mine!" shouted the demon. The web broke as he uttered the words. The demon fell back into hell.

Spirituality is as thin and as fragile as a spider's web but it is strong enough to hold all of humanity unless I think it is mine.

Dealing with Parenting Issues. Some of the issues that Iraq and Afghanistan veterans present will have to do with parenting. Their parenting skills may have been seriously damaged by their combat experiences.

Combat veterans are disturbed by not only having killed a child, but also by witnessing the grief of the child's mother. The memory of the child's face, combined with the mother's grief, haunts veterans, and will be restimulated when their own children reach that age. Veterans need help to be prepared for that event.

Therapists can help with that preparation by asking veterans to visualize their child reaching that age.

"What will your child be like at that age? What do you imagine, when you imagine the future? How is it possible to reconcile the guilt, sadness, and anger of having to kill a child with the love and devotion you feel for your own child?" These are critical issues that, if not confronted now, will challenge and torment the veteran in future years.

However, since children tend to imitate their parents, just the symptoms of PTSD significantly influence children's development. Children do not discriminate between what is psychologically inept (the symptoms) and what is psychologically effective in their parent's behavior. Even if the child goes through a clear psychological individuation at puberty, much of the parental influence will always remain in terms of behavior.

This is called "secondary PTSD." Children learn certain behaviors (e.g., easily angered, socially isolated) based on the experience of their parents' symptoms.

As a result of U.S. wars, we now have multiple generations of individuals with PTSD. Many individuals who have never seen combat or had anything traumatic directly occur have all of the symptoms of PTSD because they had a parent with PTSD.

When veterans express their difficulty with being a parent, it is important to help them see the relationship between this difficulty and their PTSD symptoms. Most important is to emphasize that the veteran does not want his or her child to struggle with the parent's symptoms of anger, depression, and anxiety.

Once awareness has occurred, it is much easier to encourage veterans to attend parenting classes. Two of my personal favorites are Parenting Effectiveness

Training (PET) and Systematic Training of Effective Parents (STEP). Most communities also offer free or minimal-payment parenting classes.

Resolving Difficult Feelings about Children Killed in War. The next step is to help veterans to resolve their anger and grief regarding the death of the Iraqi child or children. This can be a long process of integration, and may never completely feel resolved. To help things along, the "empty chair" technique, (in which an empty chair is used as a way of helping the veteran talk to the child) can be very effective. This technique can be combined with encouraging the veteran to do a drawing of the child, a meditation on the child, and a ritual of asking for and giving forgiveness.

Many times, veterans will harbor significant anger regarding the child's actions that forced them to kill him or her. That anger needs to be accepted and seen as a valid response. Veterans may resist this awareness, in their need to be honest with themselves. They will assert that the child was too young to know what he or she was doing. Yet while that is true, it is also true that veterans did not have a choice. It was a matter of either kill the child or be killed along with many of the other soldiers.

A New Relationship to God. Veterans are usually open for a spiritual insight during these moments. They may feel and believe that they are no longer able to access a connection with their current concept of God. If possible, a gradual challenge to that concept is helpful.

It was a late night at the Vet Center. The group of Iraq veterans had been meeting for several weeks, and were beginning to find common ground in their difficulties. But one of the men, Donald, struggled with guilt over killing women and children when his patrol had been attacked. "I really don't know what I'm going to do," he said as he stared at the floor. "I mean, I can't go to Mass, but I can't hide. I don't know what to do."

The other young men shifted uneasily in their chairs. Talk of religion always created a certain amount of discomfort.

"Maybe God's not like that," I offered.

"What do you mean?" asked Donald.

"Is there another way of thinking about God? I mean, who really knows? We have a lot of authorities and books that tell us things, but nobody *really* knows. Do they?" I was taking a chance with this but it seemed worth it.

"I can't make up my own version of God just to suit me," said Donald, looking impatient. "I could make God be any way I want Him. How is that helpful?"

"It sounds like you need to punish yourself, and you are using God as an excuse. Doesn't the *church* create a version of God that suits them? You're trying to be honest. Trust yourself to create a God that is more forgiving and loving, yet will also hold you accountable for things you don't want to do. The real issue, here, is that you did not have a choice in Iraq. But you need to feel absolved from what you consider a crime against yourself. It seems to me that rituals like Mass and confession are all instruments used for just this purpose of absolution. But you can create your own rituals. You do not have to have the priest as the middle man."

I paused for a while, carefully watching Donald. He continued to look at the floor. The rest of the group was silent. Finally, I turned to one of them and asked, "What is it like for you to listen to this?"

The young man said, "The Iraqis were assholes. They didn't care about their kids. I mean, I saw fathers bring in their daughters to the medics with third-degree burns—and the *father* had done it. To his own child! Iraqis are stupid assholes."

Donald looked up at the other man. "Yeah, but that's them. This is me. I killed them. I shot them. I'm no better."

The other veteran looked back at him. "Get over it. We all had to do things. It was fucking war."

I interjected, "Donald, how long do you think you will have to punish yourself?"

He looked disgusted.

I said, "OK, tell us about what happened. I want to hear all the details right from the beginning."

We had heard his account before, and he had expressed a great deal of emotion; but it was important to hear it again, and possibly again, and possibly even again, until Donald had actually integrated his necessity for having done this act of war.

Chapter Three
Posttraumatic Growth

The plain truth is too simple for the seeker after complexity, who is looking for things he cannot understand.[1]

Hazrat Inayat Khan

Posttraumatic Growth (PTG) is not a new idea. As was pointed out in the Introduction, ancient texts such as the Bhagavad Gita discuss how severe combat trauma can lead one to the depths of the soul.

Karen Armstrong describes in *The Great Transformation*[2] the beginning of every religion and how they are catalyzed by traumatic episodes. Zarathustra witnessed the barbaric pillaging of villages and began Zoroastrianism. Siddhartha Gautama was shocked by the revelation of old age, sickness, and suffering. He became the Buddha. Jesus was flogged and crucified, transcended death and became the living Christ.

How could this happen? How is it possible that horrible traumatic events can transform individuals and transcend ordinary ways of seeing the world?

---

1 Inayat Khan, *The Complete Sayings of Hazrat Inayat Khan* (New Lebanon Omega Publications, 2010), 253.
2 Armstrong, Karen, *The Great Transformation: The Beginning of Our Religious Traditions* (New York: Knopf, 2006).

Reorganization of the Nafs

The complex interactions of the nafs construct our egos, limit our growth, and narrow our perspectives. Our egos, in turn, direct our views of the world.

Posttraumatic Growth (PTG) is the result of an improved reorganization of the nafs. The ego is given a new perspective, and beliefs regarding the world and veterans' places in it have become greater. Because of the reorganization of the nafs there have been changes in how veterans view themselves and their world.

Those changes have included increases in emotional strength, a greater appreciation of life, gratitude for what has happened, and an ability to see the value in what others define as tragedies. This is not just "That which does not kill me makes me stronger," but a moving into a realization of greater realities.

The psychological literature focuses on measurements of cognitive and behavioral change to determine the existence of PTG.[3] Self-Report surveys such as the Posttraumatic Growth Inventory[4] are used to provide evidence regarding the presence or absence of PTG. The Inventory covers such seemingly diverse areas as: relating to others, new possibilities, personal strength, spiritual change, and appreciation of life.

---

3 Shakespeare-Finch, J. and A. Barrington. "Behavioral Changes Add Validity to the Construct of Posttraumatic Growth." *Journal of Traumatic Stress*, August, 25, 2012, 433-439.

4 R.G. Tedeschi, R.G. and L.G. Calhoun. "The Posttraumatic Growth Inventory: Measuring the Positive Legacy of Trauma." *Journal of Traumatic Stress*. 9, 1996, 455-471.

It is the nature of science to want to reduce processes of life into manageable compartments. To view all of those aspects of the person as a spiritual process would be quickly dismissed by researchers.

For Posttraumatic Growth to occur in veterans as a result of treatment, it is necessary that the nafs need to reorganize in a more effective and evolved manner, after their traumatic dispersal. If veterans are given adequate treatment, this reorganization of nafs may occur in a way that improves their ability to function—both internally within their self-concept, and externally in the world, as an individual. The more general goals of treatment are to help veterans regain their prewar beliefs, or to incorporate the lessons learned from combat into the realizations that the world is inherently violent and dangerous. PTG focuses on valid perceptions of the external world as challenging yet stimulating, and the internal world as able to create coherent experiences from traumas.

The Golden Rule. As the organization of the nafs improves, the ego structures become less self-centered and begin to orient towards compassion for others. Certainly, the ancient rule of "Do unto others as you would have others do unto you" is the signpost of a civilized society.

As Karen Armstrong points out in *The Great Transformation*,[5] some version of the Golden Rule is the thread that ties all religions. Personally, the attempt to treat others as I would like to be treated is an ideal that I find inspiring in the abstract, but difficult to

---

5 Armstrong, Karen, *The Great Transformation: The Beginning of Our Religious Traditions* (New York: Knopf, 2006).

follow in reality. My nafs continually return me to my own needs and my resistance to the Rule. However, Armstrong also asserts that simply *thinking* of the Rule is already a form of transcendence beyond our ordinary daily routine. As one of my friends/teachers put it, "Rules are for fools—and as long as I am a fool, I need the rule."

Certainly, following the Rule is no less a challenge for veterans. If they are successful in even occasionally being aware of the Rule, one could propose that they have begun to show PTG.

Shifting What Is Important. It is possible to get an idea about the level of veterans' nafs by asking them, "What is important to you?"

What is actually important is not always what seems to be important. Veterans may appear to have elevated drugs and alcohol to a status of importance. But those substances may be masking a disillusionment of more refined nafs, such as, compassion, altruism, sensitivity, and inspiration.

Dave tried not to think about his time in Vietnam. He drank, used a variety of drugs (some prescribed and some not on the VA's pharmaceutical list), and looked for violent physical interaction with another male. It didn't matter whether the other person was large or small; whether Dave was the last one standing or the one left on the ground. What mattered was that the physical pain from the fights overwhelmed the emotional pain of his memories.

Dave lived in a small town famous for a beach that allowed camping. At night, he went to a local bar and restaurant that had a popular reputation among the campers. Dave presented a calm, non-threatening appearance as he sat at the bar nursing a beer. His general demeanor and attitude seemed friendly, and the conversation he started up with the nearest man seemed genial.

Then things would take a sudden and surprising shift. Dave would make a comment regarding the other man's sexual preference. The unhappy camper would either succumb to his own violent temper by standing up and returning the apparent insult, or would attempt to move away from Dave. The first option was Dave's favorite. In that scenario, he and the angry camper would step into the alley behind the bar, where the fight would usually be quick and painful. If Dave was still standing, he very much enjoyed kicking the individual on the ground.

And if the camper chose Option Two, Dave was quick to escalate his insults. If the camper continued to move away, Dave was not above following the man and trying to get him to turn and throw a punch. In this way, Dave lived and floated through a haze of pain, beer, and drugs.

One evening, a camper had chosen Option One, and Dave had happily obliged. But he sensed something strange about this camper—something he couldn't put his finger on.

Usually, Dave was able to get in the first punch— the deciding factor. As the two would circle each other in the alley, Dave would pretend to back down, throwing the other man off guard. Then, if the other man relaxed his guard and gave Dave an opening, Dave would step forward and quickly hit the other man in the stomach. This would render the man momentarily helpless—a situation that Dave would take advantage of with a few more punches and strategically placed kicks. Then he would return to the bar and have a few more for the road.

This particular man did not relax his guard, and the fight was on. Yet even during the bloody violence of the fight, Dave felt that the man reminded him of someone. Not until Dave had his hands around the man's throat did the image of a friend from Vietnam having his head splattered by another Marine's round suddenly insert itself. Shaken, Dave dropped the man and staggered away from the alley.

Dave spent the next several days trying to get away from himself, but his normal ways of trying to escape were less effective than usual. Finally, he took the advice of his only friend and called his local Vet Center.

When Dave came in for treatment, he was angry and violent. At the same time, he realized that if he continued searching for deadening pain, he would end up spending the rest of his life in prison. He was clutching at straws.

At the beginning, I explained to him how we would proceed, gave him a list of articles and books to read, and told him what to expect. He seemed like someone who had reached the end and was now willing to try anything.

We worked our way through his childhood and his very successful athletic career. He had been drafted by the Army and then assigned to the Marines. Boot camp had been at the infamous Parris Island, and his descriptions of the violent attacks by the D.I.s were some of the worst I had heard. As we began going into his journey through Vietnam, I could see that Dave had begun to sober up. There were no more hangovers during the sessions, and his temper had begun to subside. He had never talked about his experiences to anyone; and to express his pain regarding the brutality of his boot camp training was cathartic.

Marines have very close ties with other Marines, and consider themselves an elite group. At the same time, they may also have a very cynical view of the Corps. As Dave would remark, "Eat the apple and fuck the Corps."

Dave's traumas had not all been in combat. There were many other incidents he related that had been violent, heart-rending, and shattering. As we continued with treatment, for the first time Dave began to look toward the future. Up till then, he had existed primarily from day to day; but now he started to become more interested in future possibilities. Vietnam had taught him to live in the present, ignore the death and destruction, and deal only with what was happening now. In treatment, the current *now* expanded to include how what he did might affect the future. When Dave thought in this way, for the first time he was also allowing the future to affect the present.

He stopped drinking completely, and his thoughts began to take on a greater clarity. His ambition returned, and he enrolled in a local university. After graduating he went on to a graduate school, where he earned a master's degree in psychology. Eventually he got a job in the Vet Center system as a counselor for other veterans. Along the way, he became interested in Buddhism and began to include meditation as one of his daily experiences.

He became someone, and his own way of being emerged.

Regaining Trust in Ideals

As veterans regain a trust in ideals and begin to acquire greater faith and strength in their convictions, their ability to interact with others becomes more effective. They begin to see the experience of vulnerability as strength rather than a liability. They begin to enjoy the sensation of being "seen." They experience a relief at no longer having to censor their thoughts and feelings.

Jim's third marriage was on the brink of disaster. He was a successful and charismatic salesman, able to charm and manipulate customers and friends into profitable, as well as risky, enterprises. In addition, he was difficult to make contact with emotionally. Glib and resourceful, he avoided any but the most superficial relationships. His cynicism was born in the battles of Vietnam, where he witnessed the seemingly cavalier waste of other soldiers' lives.

As he related to me in treatment, "They would send us out to probe the NVA. You know what that means? It means that they didn't expect us to come back—and then they would know how strong and where the gooks were. The command didn't give a shit. We were meaningless to them. Our lives were expendable."

When Jim began to actually move into his sense of reality of Vietnam, he began to drop his cynicism. He began to perceive that his need to never trust and to always believe the worst of people was the result of the betrayal he had experienced in Vietnam. His cynicism had developed in order to protect him from disappointment and feelings of humiliation at being duped. Gradually, he came to realize that what others did was not as important as what *he* did. His depression and anger was primarily about how he had become, and his resentment was in his blaming others for himself. He avoided responsibility for how he felt and what he did.

Now he began to take responsibility for his emotions, and began to enjoy letting his wife and children see how he believed he was. He let them know what he thought and how he saw the world. The more he revealed, the more he felt understood and the less angry he felt.

Pain of Loss; Joy of Caring

As the nafs become reorganized, veterans' hearts open, risking the pain of loss and the joy of caring. Ideals of innocence are revisited, this time with an awareness of fallibility and an understanding of the power of forgiveness. Balancing greater flexibility with the rigorousness of truth, veterans also open to a love of beauty. Having seen the extremes of government-sanctioned violence, they embrace the new *imago mundi* (worldview) of the immanence within the transcendence: finding God within the physical.

When I am lost in Your Transcendence, You reveal Your Immanence. When I am lost in Your Immanence, You reveal Your Transcendence.[6]

---

6 Pir Vilayat Inayat Khan's restating of a classic Sufi text.

Walt served three tours in Iraq. He was good at what he did, and was dedicated to his soldiers. The other soldiers listened to him and paid attention to his admonitions and understanding. But when Walt came home, he was unable to adapt to the stateside military, and requested a discharge.

Once back home, he tried to return to school; but his concentration was constantly interrupted by his memories of the victories and losses in Iraq, and he became reclusive.

He sought out other veterans on campus, but even in the group of veterans he felt alone and longed for his former military position of authority. He began to skip classes and dull his experiences with alcohol.

By the time he came in for treatment, he was in despair and longing to return to the war.

"This is really humiliating," he admitted. "I never thought I would come in to see a psychologist. I never thought bad of the guys who went to mental health, but I never thought I would need to."

As we worked through his experiences, he began to integrate what lay behind the traumas. His way of seeing his life changed from one of confusion to one of seeing a continuum of process.

"It seems like there's a purpose behind all of this," he mused. "When I got back from my final tour, I felt like life was sort of what happened to me. Now, it's more like I have choices. There are ways of living, and I can choose how I want to be. Seeing the way people live in Iraq—they were happy. Well, at least some of them."

Walt continued, "You couldn't trust anybody, except maybe this one guy who was our translator. Most of the Iraqis were like children. At first I thought they were just stupid. Then I realized that they weren't used to taking care of themselves. Their government had kept them like children, so they wouldn't gain power. Of course, there were some people who knew what was going on and took advantage of the opportunities."

He paused and then said, "I come back here, and it's like this culture has nothing but children. People walking around like nothing bad could happen to them. They don't know, and it's because they're protected. I've had the opportunity to see what it's like to not be protected but to be a *protector*. I liked being the protector, and I still miss it. But there's more to it than that. I know something that most people don't know. Even other vets I talk to don't seem to get it. They talk about the military and the weapons and the bullshit—and that's all fine; but that's not all. I don't *want* that part of my life to have been the best part. I want to understand why I am *here*. I believe that my life—shit, I think *anyone's* life—has so much."

Now his face changed to a look of hope and wonder. "This may be weird, but when I was wounded in that IED explosion, I felt like I left my body and went way up. I was above the explosion and could look down at what had just happened. I've never told anybody this. It gave me the idea that there's a lot more to life than what I think."

Walt went on to major in comparative religion at a local university. After graduating, he was admitted into a graduate program. He was someone who was able to incorporate his wartime experiences and use them to find a greater depth in life.

It may be true that, as the Sufis point out, we are a thought in the mind of God. God thinks—and this is what happens. There may be a part of God that is un-conscious—a part that doesn't know it is God. That's us. *We* are the unconscious part of God, and our purpose is to become conscious of being God. As we become conscious, God becomes conscious. The Sufi Ibn Arabi says that God condescended to descend from the solitude of his unity out of love, so that each of His parts might know His perfection.[7]

Compassion

The thousands of veterans I have seen over the last three decades have impressed me with their courage and hope—but most of all, with their compassion.

Liz had joined the Marines to get away from her abusive parents. She had been part of a Quick Reaction Force (QRF), a group that would come to the aid of other troops under attack, in Iraq. She earned a combat action badge (CAB) because of her courage in braving an ambush and putting down covering fire for the troops. Now, in treatment, she struggled with resentment, frustration, and anger with not being given her due.

"Guys and women all assume that I was some sort of support troop. Even other vets think of me as a lightweight, until they see I got a CAB."

"How do you work with that?" I asked her.

"I know that combat is a big macho thing, and to think that a woman could do it is a real threat to their egos. And a lot of women don't think I should have

7 See Chittick, William, *The Self-Disclosure of God: Principles of Ibn al-'Arabi's Cosmology* (Albany: SUNY Press, 1998).

done it—it puts them at risk. Actually, I get more crap from other women than I do from the guys."

"Sounds like you don't get much support."

"Right," she agreed. "But that's the deal. When I was in the military, I got hit on by other women a lot more than I did by the men. There was a whole group of women, and if you weren't one of them it just didn't happen for you."

"You mean you didn't get rank and other types of duty."

"Not only that. I got assigned to the combat unit—which was exactly what I wanted. Now I know what I can do." She sighed and looked at the floor. There was long pause.

"You must feel alone."

"Yeah. I've found out that it doesn't work to push this. People pull away. I understand that. So I don't talk much about it, especially to other vets. If they ask, I tell them about the QRF—but most of the time they want to tell me about what happened to them. And that's OK. I can see that they're hurting a lot more than I am. I have an advantage because I had nothing to prove. But I got a chance to see this bullshit up close."

Liz now became emotional. "This whole killing, this tearing apart bodies, ending lives, people you don't even know—it's fucked up. They were trying to kill us, but we were in their country. It doesn't matter. I signed on to the military, so I knew what the job might be going in. I got away from my family and I had an incredible experience. That was something I will never forget."

Liz added her military combat experience to her already deep knowledge of the world. Somehow, she was able to avoid the pessimistic and cynical attitude that characterized so many other women in the military. While her experience of being harassed by her own gender was difficult, it is much more common for women to be not only harassed by men in the military, but to also be sexually assaulted.

"You know," she realized, "there are better ways to help. So I'm studying other languages. I want to speak to people in other cultures. I'm through with being arrogant. Yes, the Iraqi women were persecuted and beaten—but so are American women."

Liz's compassion for the downtrodden extended beyond gender. She became strong and independent because of her realizations of herself. Those realizations were catalyzed by her military traumas. She came into treatment with an inner strength and intelligence that enabled us to further strengthen her understanding.

Coming to Peace

Jim was different. He had isolated himself after the Vietnam War. A Marine, he had experienced many fire fights and one horrendous battle with the NVA. His small convoy had come around a corner in the road, face-to-face with a battalion of NVA. After half the convoy was lost, F-4 jets finally dropped napalm so close that Jim told me, "I was lying under a jeep and the explosion just sucked the air out of my body. I had never felt such intense heat." The napalm drove the NVA back sufficiently that the remnants of the convoy were able to get inside the perimeter of the nearest Marine base.

Jim arrived at the stateside Marine base many months later. It was 1970, and the protesters were about a hundred strong, surrounding and blocking the entrance gate. The bus Jim was on had about twenty grunts fresh from the jungles, rice paddies, terror, grief, and bloodshed. The men looked at the screaming crowd outside the bus. Finally, the gunnery sergeant stood up and said, "Well, this is sure a bunch of shit. But this is what we are fighting for! Let's go through the motherfuckers!"

Following the gunnery's lead, the Marines pushed their way through the crowd until they were able to gain entrance to the base. Years later, Jim related that he wasn't sure which had been more horrible— the NVA, or the protesters. Yes, the NVA was trying to kill him; but the action of his country hurt more deeply. This reception upon returning home is called "sanctuary trauma."

After a year of individual work in therapy, Jim then was in a group for two more years. At the end of his treatment, he had decided to marry and attend college, and he had a wide circle of friends. He had resolved his hurt and grief over his sanctuary trauma. He said, "I understand that everyone does things according to their conscience. I went to war because I believed that the country needed my help. There were a lot of people who believed the opposite, and for some reason they wanted to punish me for what I had done. While it still seems like a bunch of crap that someone who believed in peace could be so hateful, I try to remember that we all make mistakes. I think I wouldn't do the same things now that I did when I was nineteen, and I hope that those protesters wouldn't do the same things now that they did then."

His Holiness the Dalai Lama points out, "Everyone wants peace. But we need a genuine peace that is founded on mutual trust and the realization that as brothers and sisters we must all live together without trying to destroy each other. Even if one nation or community dislikes another, they have no alternative but to live together. And under the circumstances it is much better to live together happily."[8]

In all battles, there is the possibility for a particularly devastating condition to occur known as the "berserker." A berserker is someone who is so overcome by the stress and fear of combat that he or she suddenly loses all fear of dying and performs many heroic acts, possibly saving many lives while killing many others. Sometimes, berserkers are is killed; but when they aren't—when they survive their periods of transcendent awareness, when their own physical lives don't matter to them—we honor them with medals and expressions of gratitude.

Jake had been just about to get on the helicopter when the lieutenant pulled him aside: "Sarge, I gotta talk to you. Take the next one." Jake got off, and the helicopter with his squad took off. The chopper got about one hundred feet off the ground when a rocket scored a direct hit. No one survived. Jake's entire squad was killed in an instant.

---

8 Dalai Lama, *Essential Teachings*, (Berkeley: North Atlantic Books,1995).

Jake went berserk. For several days, he became a one-man killing force. Machine gun fire, mortars, rockets, meant nothing, as he no longer cared about living or dying. Only killing as many of the enemy meant anything. Finally, Command relieved him of his duty and reassigned him to a non-combat post. Ironically, he was assigned to grave registration, where he made sure that bodies had the proper designation regarding name, rank, and serial number. Sometimes it is difficult to fathom military thinking, or just the insensitivity of military bureaucracy.

Jake came in for treatment after spending a decade, post-discharge, as a homeless alcoholic. He was a very intelligent person, well-read though undereducated. In therapy, he worked out his war, his homecoming, his anger, his violence, his grief, his self-hatred, and his hopes. He became interested in mystical awareness, and began to practice the ancient arts of prayer and meditation.

He obtained a master's degree in education and a teaching job. He married and had children. He found a place in his heart for everyone, and published a book on poetry. Here is one of his poems:

Mike Torrelli Died Today

I watched Mike Torelli die today.
I felt his warm life leak out all over
my pants as I held his head in my lap
and looked into his young eyes—
questioning.
Why me he seemed to say why me?
I have no answers for him, I don't know

why he was the one the bullet picked
to rip and tear and hurt.

I asked him if he was alright, meaning
was he in pain, but instead—he said
that as near as he could tell he had
made his peace with God and everything
would be OK.

I wonder how a nineteen year old
Marine from the South Bronx could
Know such things.

Outside the Bottle

Our lives are brief in terms of history, and endless in terms of creation. I don't know what awaits, but I have faith that is strengthened as I breathe my life. I see veterans and I know that they have been granted a great wisdom. They are like the giant who is unaware of his strength.

The fly that is in the bottle doesn't see the way out; but if we stand outside the bottle, we can see the opening.

We are outside the bottle. We can help those trapped inside.

APPENDIX

Appendix

Helping Veterans Establish PTSD Service-Connected Disability Claims with the U.S. Department of Veterans Affairs

You would think that filing a claim with the Veterans Administration (VA) for a service-connected disability would be straightforward. That's a joke, although not a very good one. Even after over thirty years of helping veterans I am still shocked by what VA benefits analysts may request from veterans.

This appendix is here to help.

Requesting money from most government bureaucracies results in a mind-numbingly dense process. With its numbers of forms, intricate mazes of requirements, deadlines for filing, deadlines for appeals, and long waits for decisions, it is overwhelming. The VA's claims process is much worse than anything you might have previously encountered or imagined. This is all the more true when veterans have to do this all on their own.

As a result of their PTSD, most veterans are financially in ruin. After burning through jobs, marriages, possible jail time, and substance abuse, the stress level of veterans is not just from the war.

Helping veterans with their claims is an integral part of treatment.

With some clear understanding and help from therapists, veterans will experience that claims process more successfully, though it probably will be no less Byzantine.

A well-known dictum for therapists goes, "If you treat, do not evaluate. If you evaluate, do not treat." My advice is: when it comes to working with veterans, forget that. I know there are good arguments for that dictum, but believe me those arguments are not applicable here.

Types of Veterans, in Terms of Claims

Regarding claims, you will see two types of veterans. One type has already filed a claim, and is coming for treatment and evaluation. The second type has not filed a claim, and is coming for treatment.

This second type can be further categorized into two sub-types:

1. **Veterans who are resistant to filing a claim.** These veterans have a variety of reasons why not to file a claim, but mostly it is, "Other guys had it a lot worse." While this reason may make sense, it is irrelevant. You can ask them, "OK, other guys had it worse. But did what happen to you as a result of serving your country disrupt your life and make it difficult for you to be happy, effective, and at peace?" If the answer is yes, then file the claim.

Other reasons have to do with not wanting the government involved in their lives. They don't trust the government and don't want to feel indebted. Again, there is nothing wrong with that reason, but they may not realize how much they can benefit from receiving VA assistance. Here, therapists' knowledge of the enormous number of benefits available for a service-connected veteran is helpful. First of all, point out the money. Most of us could use a tidy stipend each month for the rest of our lives. Secondly, list the lifetime health care at the VA, paid tuition at state colleges and universities for dependents, lowered property taxes, free passes to state parks, vocational rehabilitation...and the list goes on.

2. **Veterans who are simply unaware of the claims process and are more than happy to file a claim.**

The Value of Filing

Both groups need to be adequately prepared for the length and complexity of the claims process. However, while a claim may take years (yes, literally years) to complete, if the claim is approved, the veteran will be paid retroactive to the time filed of filing. This is really important to point out. Even if the claim takes two years to decide, the veteran will receive two years' worth of payments in a lump sum. Therefore filing as soon as possible is essential.

Where To File

Where do they file? Personally, I am most familiar with California. The best place there is with the County Veterans Service Officer (CVSO).

Note that the CVSO does not work for the VA. He or she is a specialist who works for the county. Their job is to assist veterans in working through the VA's bureaucracy, and they can be of inestimable help.

However, the CVSO can also be a roadblock. Some Service Officers will not file claims if they don't think that the claim is viable. Other Service Officers have delusions of being a psychologist, and think they can determine whether someone has PTSD. Others will not file a claim if veterans don't have an award that signifies they were in combat (Combat Infantry Badge for the Army, Combat Action Ribbon for the Marines, Purple Heart, etc.). In regard to the issue of proving combat, President Obama signed a Regulatory Revision in 2010 that stated if a service person had been in a theater of operations and a VA psychiatrist or a VA psychologist diagnosed them with PTSD, no further proof of trauma was needed. All that was needed was to determine the percent of disability.

Finally there are many CVSOs who just don't do their job. I know that is hard to believe, but my experience over the last thirty years has involved working with many different CVSOs—and yes, there truly are many who don't do anything.

Assuming that your CVSO does work on behalf of veterans, it still is the Service Officer's job to file the claim and aid in the claims process—not to determine a claim's viability, whether the veteran has PTSD, or what the veteran may be entitled to. (You may have noticed that I am slightly touchy about this subject.)

What To Do After Filing the Claim

The "Statement in Support of" Claim. After the claim has been filed, veterans will receive a letter from the VA stating that they have received the claim, and requesting a "Statement in Support of Claim." This Statement is an important document; therapists need to go over veterans' statements carefully.

There are two kinds of Statements, depending on the veteran.

One kind of Statement is from *veterans who have the necessary documents proving combat*. The VA will concede (i.e., acknowledge) that the appropriate stressors are documented, and therefore, the Statement needs not so much to detail the combat but instead to focus on the degree to which that combat now interferes in veterans' lives.

The second kind is much more complex. Even with recent regulatory revision, it may be still difficult to verify the necessary level of combat for the appropriate award.

I am currently working with a veteran where the VA has continually denied his claim. The case is now entering its fourth year. As a soldier, the veteran was stationed in the Philippines during the Vietnam War, but was frequently flown to Vietnam to work on helicopters. While in Vietnam, he was told to go on Medivacs (pulling out wounded from hot LZs) with the helicopters. This soldier had innumerable experiences under fire, helping the wounded, and having soldiers die in his arms.

The VA initially denied that the veteran was ever in Vietnam. We secured the veteran's 201 file (complete service file), which documented his duty in Vietnam. However, the file did not list the veteran's Medivac experiences. The VA—in probably the most egregious reply I have ever seen—then asked this veteran for the name of one of the soldiers who died in the helicopter. Note that this was over thirty years ago! Soldiers did not have names on their uniforms; there may not even have been dog tags; the chaos and blood in the helicopter was overwhelming; and, as I said, it was thirty years ago.

Filing a Report by the Therapist. After helping veterans with their Statement, it is vital that you file a report. In my reports, I include diagnostic tests relevant to the disorder (there are many different types of tests that focus on PTSD). The report needs to focus on how PTSD has impacted veterans' lives, detailing everything that a psychological evaluation includes.

If the Claim Is Approved

If the claim is approved, it will award the veteran a certain percentage of disability. This percentage is based on criteria the VA uses to assess the degree the veteran's difficulties interfere with their lives. This percentage for PTSD may be combined with other disabilities (tinnitus, back problems, etc.). However, if the veteran is awarded 30% for PTSD, 10% for tinnitus, and 20% for back problems, those figures do not necessarily add up to 60%. I understand this is a confusing point, and I am not much help in clearing it up. This is VA math, and I have never understood how they figure the final percentage.

Filing a Notice of Disagreement

However, as long as the percentage is less than 100%, veterans may believe that the award is not sufficient, and file a Notice of Disagreement.

This requires another supplementary report, in which you argue with the reasons for whatever percentage was awarded cited in the VA Award Letter. Do not give up. Persevere. Regardless of what the claims officers, Board of Veterans Appeals, and other bureaucrats tell you, don't give up. It is our job to convince them of the validity of our perspective.

If the claim is denied, the same process applies as indicated above. In other words, file another report.

The VA goes by the rule of "The Benefit of the Doubt." This states that if there is any doubt in the case, the benefit goes to the veteran. "The Benefit of the Doubt" is an excellent rule, which should be invoked when push comes to shove.

Therapists need to be prepared to appear in front of the Board of Veterans Appeals, along with the veteran. I have done this several times and have found the Board to be fair, interested in determining the truth, and very helpful. My impression is, of course, based on the fact that every time I have appeared the veteran was awarded the maximum (100%).

Preparing Veterans for a Change in Self-Identity

Finally, therapists need to help prepare veterans for a change in self-identity, which will occur upon receipt of the award letter. It is one thing to be diagnosed as having PTSD. It is quite another to have the Department of Veterans Affairs write you a letter telling you that you are 100% disabled, and they are going to send you money for that disability for the rest of your life.

The psychological impact of this award cannot be overstated, both in terms of veterans' self-concepts and self-directions. This is important work that can be used to help in PTG. A refusal to accept labels, understanding the language of diagnosis and disability, and the understanding of the aid in recovery are powerful tools for veterans.

Good luck. And again, *Don't Give Up!*

GLOSSARY

Note: This glossary contains the important terms mentioned in the book that have to do with things military, psychological, and spiritual.

A

Accommodation:

• The development of insights in the expansion of the self-concept that allow the integration of the traumatic experience into the expanded belief systems (see also *Circulatio*).

• An internal method of organization, according to Piaget. (1) When new information does not require too great a change in our beliefs, we simply change the beliefs. (2) When we are not able to change the beliefs, we change the information.

AIT: Advanced Individual Training

Alchemy:

(1) A process by which there is a transformation of the personality as a result of traumatic experiences.

(2) A dynamic transcendence that awakens our inner depths.

(3) The transformation of the human personality from an impure, selfish state, directed by constant desires and greed, into a pure state epitomized by kindness, patience, love, and a desire only to serve the One.

(4) The transformation of the ego from a solid selfish state to an open compassionate process.

(5) *Ars regia* (the royal art).

Alchemical process:
- The dissolution (*solve*) and reforming (*coagule*) of the ego.
- *Nigredo/Separatio*: The phase of the alchemical process where, through trauma plunging soldiers into a psychological state where nothing makes sense (nigredo), the nafs are scattered; the individual's ego reality is completely disrupted (separatio).
- *Coagule*: The rebuilding of the self.
- *Sublimatio*: Rising above the chaos of the solve; a direct experience of the ideal self.
- *Circulatio*: The process of rising above, and then returning to the solve, and then another sublimatio. Psychologically experienced as the development of insights in the expansion of the self-concept that allow the integration of the traumatic experience into the expanded belief systems (also known as "accommodation").

Anger:
- An expression of pain. Veterans' suffering has to be brought into awareness if their anger is going to be reduced.
- A coping response to increased stress.
- An expression of a need. All needs are a form of prayer.

Anger, alternatives to:
- Cleaning and organizing
- Problem-solving discussions

Anger Journal: A journaling method for veterans to learn to cope with anger.

Anxiety list: Used in reducing anxiety

Ars regia (**the royal art**): Alchemy.

ARVNs: The Army of the Republic of Vietnam.

Assimilation: An internal method of organization. According to Piaget, what takes place when our belief systems are adequate to incorporate the new information.

Awards, military:
- Combat Infantry Badge (Army).
- Combat Action Ribbon (Marines).
- Purple Heart.

B

Banana clips: The use of clips of ammunition in the AK47.

Base of operations: The base where the veteran is stationed.

"Benefit of the Doubt" rule: VA policy that if there is any doubt in the case, the benefit goes to the veteran.

Berserker: Someone in wartime who is so overcome by the stress and fear of combat that he or she suddenly loses all fear of dying and performs many heroic acts, possibly saving many lives while killing many others.

Bradley fighting machine: An armored military vehicle used in Iraq.

Burnout, in therapists: The therapist begins to demonstrate similar symptoms to PTSD.

C

C-rations: Military ration foods of various kinds.

CAB: Combat Action Badge (Marines).

CIB: Combat Infantryman's Badge (Army).

Cathartic therapy: A therapy based on the expression of anger—a very dangerous approach with veterans, as it can open up violent acting out.

Chronological sequence of exploration in treatment: Childhood; adolescence; entry into the military; basic training; advanced training ; deployment; return home.

Circulatio: The process of rising above, and then returning to the solve, and then another sublimatio. Psychologically experienced as the development of insights in the expansion of the self-concept that allow the integration of the traumatic experience into the expanded belief systems (also known as "accommo-dation").

Coagule: Alchemical stage involving the rebuilding of the self.

Combat PTSD, treatment of: Directed at reorganiz-ing the nafs (i.e., improving ego development) into a dynamic system that integrates the traumatic infor-mation through the expansion of beliefs.

Compassion fatigue: *See* Burnout.

Concentration: The process of holding a certain idea or object in the mind at all times.

Coping skills, developing: Skills that help in the treatment.

County Veterans Service Officer (CVSO): A specialist who works for the county whose job is to assist veterans in working through the VA's bureau-cracy when filing a disability claim.

D

Decompensation: A process of ego breakdown that results in the development of serious emotional difficulties such as psychosis

Demanding Self (*nafs al-ammara*): The self that insists on its prerogatives, demands every privilege and priority and cannot recognize anyone except itself.

Deployment, means of: How veterans were sent to the battle (by ship, boat, plane, etc.).

DEROS: Date of Expected Return from Overseas. For the Army, after twelve months, and for the Marines, after thirteen months. Cited frequently by the North Vietnamese Officers as a primary reason for their ability force the American forces to leave.

Dismount: A soldier whose duty is to provide small arms fire to the Bradley.

E

Ego change, dynamic process of. *See* Alchemical process.

Ego development: The ego is constructed by the combination of several different levels of nafs, through which the world is filtered and our beliefs are developed. The increase of understanding by the nafs is the basis of ego development. In this system, the more advanced the ego development, the greater our understanding of existence.

Ego ideal: That towards which the ego strives, yearns to become, to merge. Contrast with "ideal ego": an idea the ego has of itself.

Ego resilience: A strong ego. This is important if the trauma is to be both integrated into, and an active catalyst in transforming, the ego.

"Empty chair" technique: A therapeutic technique used for an internal conversation.

Esprit de corps: The general morale.

Exposure treatment: A detailed remembering and retelling of the traumas.

Eye Movement Desensitization Reprocessing (EMDR): A technique that uses eye movement to decrease PTSD.

F

Fear: An adrenaline experience.

Feeling questions, avoiding asking veterans: Instead of asking veterans, "How are you feeling?" ask questions like "How are you? What is this like for you? What is it like to talk about this?" These will encourage veterans to relate in more physical, experiential language.

Floridity: Active symptoms.

Fluid beliefs: A flexible reality is needed for an accommodation of beliefs to occur.

FOBBIT: Someone who never left the Forward Operating Base.

Forgiveness: Understanding and opening the heart.

G

Generalization, law of: "when anxiety increases, generalization increases" (the tendency to generalize from one situation to another).

God-ideal: The formation of the greater Self.

Golden Rule: "Do unto others as you would have others do unto you."

Grounding techniques: Techniques used to help veterans come into a more calm, trusting place, e.g.:
- Safe memory
- Visualizing protectors
- Anchoring breath

Grunts: Infantrymen.

H

High-arousal states: Creates anxiety difficulties.

"How did that make you feel?": A question never to ask veterans. No one "makes" them feel. Instead, ask, "What was that like for you? How did you experience that? When that happened, what was happening for you? What was your experience?"

Hypervigilance: The need to be always alert, when continued into civilian life.

I

Ideal ego: An idea the ego has of itself. Contrast with "ego ideal": That towards which the ego strives, yearns to become, to merge.

Ideal self:
- Bringing to our consciousness our greatest and most profound beliefs, so veterans can begin to imagine that this ideal is part of who they are—dormant, possibly, but still within them.
- Includes the experience of acting out of innate awareness—a soul awareness—rather than the ordinary self formed from interaction with the world.

IED: Improvised explosive device.

Immanence: The presence of God in the now.

Inayat Khan, Hazrat: Sufi teacher

Pir Vilayat Inayat Khan, Pir Vilayat : Sufi teacher; son of Hazrat Inayat Khan.

Pir Zia Inayat-Khan, Pir Zia: Sufi teacher; son of Pir Vilayat Inayat Khan.

K

K-rations: Military food

L

LRP: Long Range Patrol. Operated mostly alone or in small two to three person teams.

LZ: Landing Zone for helicopters.

M

M14: Older rifle

M16: Newer rifle

M60 machine gun: Used primarily in helicopters.

Magnetism:
- Physical
- Mental
- Heart
- Soul

Manure of experience: A Buddhist term that refers to the use of difficult emotions.

Medivac: The removal of the wounded.

MRE: Meals Ready to Eat.

MOS: Military Occupation Specialty

Mysticism: For the purpose of this book, a term

used to represent the process of discovering our purpose in our manifestation.

N

Nafs: The ego's dynamic, interactive building blocks. The type of nafs that are most present represents a person's level of evolution.

- *Nafs al-ammara:* The Demanding Self—the self that insists on its prerogatives, demands every privilege and priority, and cannot recognize anyone except itself.
- *Nafs al-lawwama:* The Self-Accusing Ego—the next stage of ego development, the critical self. Self-centered in terms of doubts, worries, and anxiety. The beginning of the conscience.

Nightmares: One of the most common symptoms of PTSD; and many times, the most disturbing.

Nightmares, treatments for:
- Dreams, working consciously with
- Therapy involving art, music, dialogue, and dream interpretation
- Inspiring images
- Inspiring spiritual images
- Encouraging positive feelings towards others

Nigredo/Separatio: The phase of the alchemical process where, through trauma plunging soldiers into a psychological state where nothing makes sense (nigredo), the nafs are scattered—the individual's ego reality is completely disrupted (separatio).

"Noble enemy" concept: Viewing one's enemy as an honorable foe worthy of battle

Notice of Disagreement: A form filed by veterans who believe the amount of money that they have been awarded by the VA is not sufficient.

P

Parenting classes for veterans: Parenting Effectiveness Training (PET) and Systematic Training of Effective Parents (STEP), etc.

Perfect Friend, The: A meditation practice that helps veterans with concentration, widening perspectives, and changing beliefs.

Positive countertransference: Positive feelings that interfere with treatment.

Posttraumatic Growth (PTG): The improvement in emotional functioning after experiencing a trauma.

Prayer: Anything that takes up your sincere, whole-hearted attention as you seek to make contact with Something beyond the ego's usual self-referential awareness. Types of prayer can include:
- Ceremonial Prayer
- Ritual Prayer
- Spontaneous Prayer
- Thanksgiving Prayer
- Repentance Prayer
- Supplication Prayer
- Invocation Prayer
- Communion Prayer

Prisoner-of-war training: Part of basic training that used a simulated capture of prisoners.

Pugil sticks: Large rods with canvas-covered rubber on both ends, used in basic training.

Purple Heart: Military award given for injury in combat.

Q

QRF: Quick Reaction Force.

R

Readjustment Counseling Service (aka "The Vet Centers"): Formed within the Department of Veterans Affairs.

Recycled squad: Individuals who were unable to successfully complete basic training were "recycled" through another session of basic training, this time with even more severe and punishing conditions.

"Regular army": Soldiers who are in the army because they enlisted.

REMF: Rear echelon motherfucker.

Resistance: The avoidance of treatment.

Riverine Force: The "brown water navy," composed of various types of watercraft, including swift boats.

RPG: Rocket-propelled grenade launcher.

S

Sanctuary trauma: The experience of danger in a place that is supposed to be safe.

Secondary PTSD: Children learn certain behaviors (e.g., easily angered, socially isolated) based on their experience of their parents' symptoms.

Self-Accusing Ego (*nafs al-lawwama*): The critical self. Self-centered in terms of doubts, worries, and anxiety. The beginning of the conscience.

Shadow: The qualities we don't like in ourselves that we unconsciously project upon others.

Solve: The first stage of alchemy—an ego-shattering; the dissolving of an idea, the changing of a self-concept.

Solve et coagule: The dissolution (solve) and reforming (coagule) of the ego.

Specialized training: Special Forces, Ranger School, Airborne, SEAL Team, and Medic/Corpsman.

"Statement in Support of" claim: A document requested of veterans by the VA after veterans have filed a disability claim. Therapists need to go over veterans' statements carefully.

Stimulus overload: Too much stimulation.

SUDS: Subjective units of distress scale; used to rate the degree of difficulty in anxiety.

Sublimatio: Rising above the chaos of the solve; a direct experience of the ideal self.

"Suck it up" factor: The willingness to experience physical pain.

Sufism: An ancient mystical school.

Suicide, interfering with the process of, in treatment: Discuss the possibility openly and specifically. This takes veterans seriously.

Suicide contract: An agreement to not commit suicide.

Survivor confusion: Veterans' complete astonishment at having survived, and not understanding why.

Survivor guilt: Feelings of guilt regarding having survived.

T

Theater of operations: Where the veteran was deployed (Vietnam, Iraq, etc.).

Transcendence: The presence of God beyond the physical now.

Transcendentalists, American: A nineteenth century American school of mysticism.

V

VC: Viet Cong.

Veterans Administration: Also called the VA; officially, the U.S. Department of Veterans Affairs.

Vet Centers (Readjustment Counseling Service): Formations within the Department of Veterans Affairs.

Vicarious traumatization: Traumatized by frequent descriptions of trauma.

W

Walking point: Being the first soldier down a trail during a patrol.

Weapons:
- Bradleys
- M14 rifle
- M16 rifle
- M60 machine gun
- RPG: Rocket-propelled grenade launcher.

At the end of the talk someone from the audience asked the Dalai Lama, "Why didn't you fight back against the Chinese?" The Dalai Lama looked down, swung his feet just a bit, then looked back at us and said with a gentle smile, "Well war is obsolete, you know." Then after a few moments, his face grave, he said, "Of course the mind can rationalize fighting back... but the heart, the heart would never understand. Then you would be divided in yourself, the heart and the mind, and the war would be inside you."

I work mostly with combat veterans and their various issues. My most recent count says that I have been doing this work (PTSD) for thirty-four years. Licensed in 1977, I started specializing in Posttraumatic Stress Disorder in 1980. Beginning as a group member in a "rap group" (I was the only non-veteran), I then led private groups, then was the clinical supervisor at a Vet Center for twenty-five years. I have now been a contract/provider with the Department of Veterans Affairs for the last six years. Along the way I was also a tenured professor at a California State university, taught for over twenty years, and published many technical articles that ranged from information processing to the spiritual nature of trauma. I initially studied Sufism with the late Sufi Master Pir Vilayat Inayat Khan in 1973 and continued until he passed on in 2004. Now I study with his son, Pir Zia Inayat-Khan.

Larry Decker, Ph.D.

For more information on Sufism see

Sufi Order International
North American Secretariat
PO Box 480
New Lebanon NY 12125
www.sufiorder.org